CORK

and the

AMERICAN CORK INDUSTRY

"There are three trees in the world whose bark yields that which is of more real value to man than all the jewels and precious stones ever dug from the earth. The cuticle of a South American tree yields the liquid which is caoutchouc, or india rubber; the bark of the Peruvian cinchona bestows quinine, and the bark of a species of live oak supplies the world with cork."

Photograph by J. Vieira Natividade.
Courtesy Junta Nacional da Cortica,
Lisbon, Portugal

BEEHIVES IN PORTUGAL

Made of cork, the outer bark of an oak tree
—Quercus Suber.

A use of cork as an insulating material which
began with the Ancients, but which Portuguese farmers still find unexcelled for the
purpose.

CORK

and the

AMERICAN CORK INDUSTRY

By

ARTHUR L. FAUBEL, PH.D.

SECRETARY OF THE CORK INSTITUTE OF AMERICA

FORMERLY ASSOCIATE PROFESSOR OF ECONOMICS

NEW YORK UNIVERSITY

REVISED EDITION

CORK INSTITUTE OF AMERICA

25 WEST FORTY-THIRD STREET

NEW YORK, N. Y.

Affiliated Associations • Cork Tile Manufacturers Association
Cork Composition Manufacturers Association • Cork Stopper
Manufacturers Association • Cork Marine Goods Manufacturers
Association • Cork Insulation Manufacturers Association

COPYRIGHT, 1938 AND 1941, BY
THE CORK INSTITUTE OF AMERICA

PRINTED IN THE UNITED STATES OF AMERICA
BY QUINN & BODEN COMPANY, INC., RAHWAY, N. J.

AUTHOR'S FOREWORD

First, and at the risk of a negative start, a word as to what this book is not. It is not an exhaustive technical treatise nor has it been written for the scientist, the engineer or the technician. Instead, it is an account of cork and the cork industry for students and the general reader.

The book is an outgrowth of my teaching experience—high school and college—plus my association with the American cork industry since 1933. With the increased emphasis on the practical and applied in modern education, particularly in the field of economics, I have noticed the need for more and more concrete material on agricultural and industrial economics. The old basic course in commercial geography has expanded into courses in commerce and industry, raw materials of commerce, commercial and economic geography and economics of industry. The various excellent text books available for these courses cannot possibly cover the details of the hundreds of individual industries which, together with agriculture and labor, make up the national economy of a country. As an evidence of the need to supplement these texts with individual industry reports I have been impressed by the number of requests I get each year from students for material on the cork industry to be used for a report in one of their courses. It was these requests which were my incentive to undertake this short study on cork and the American cork industry.

It seemed to me too that such a study should answer the question I am so often asked: "What is cork, anyway?" And so I have also tried to answer this question for both the general reader and the student in physics and chemistry, but the latter will find that cork is still a challenge.

If what I have written reads like the work of a partisan, I frankly admit that it is. Cork, of course, has its limitations, but with them all, it has always impressed me as a truly remarkable product of Nature made even more so by man's ingenuity and inventive genius. I can only hope that this book will justify my enthusiasm and that it will fulfill its purposes.

Many men in the American cork industry have helped me in the preparation of this book. I gratefully acknowledge my indebtedness to each of them, and I wish that a decision of policy—the avoidance of all individual company names—did not require that all these men remain anonymous. I also acknowledge the untiring help of my wife and of my secretaries, Miss Marie B. Krtil and Miss Ethel S. Hall. I, alone, am responsible for any shortcomings in the book, and I shall welcome suggestions for its improvement.

A. L. F.

New York
April, 1938

NOTE TO THE REVISED EDITION

Three years have elapsed since the first edition of this book was published. Several months ago, as copies became increasingly scarce, we decided that a revised edition was needed. Here it is and we shall be more than satisfied if this new edition is given the same gratifying reception accorded the first.

The changes are not many. The latest statistics (through 1940 wherever possible) are included. Cork, instead of being a typical peace-time commodity, is now a material of war—see Appendix C. California-grown cork "made" the newspapers in the summer and fall of 1940—see Appendix D. The uncertainty concerning the founding of the cork industry in the United States has been cleared up—see Appendix E. The significance of the new frontispiece illustration is indicated by the inclusion in Appendix B of a brief description and report of results on a most important testing program.

In Appendix D there is a reference to a Brazilian cork substitute—the bark of the Pao Santo. Right now there is a flurry of interest in the possibility of substituting this Brazilian product for genuine cork, but the prospects are not very promising on account of cost and the limited quantity of Pao Santo bark that can be made available.

For years I have wondered about the origin of the word "corker," which Webster defines as "a person or thing of an extraordinary or remarkable kind." I wonder no more, thanks to an Englishman and an advertisement he ran in an American magazine early in 1939. This gentleman has (or had) access to "a fine old cork tree" which he reports as having been growing in England "for the past 300 years." Now the remarkable thing about this tree is its apparent capacity to work miracles ranging from healing the sick "at the time of the Great Plague of London in 1665" to help in winning a Buick automobile. In ye olden days, it was necessary for the sick and the gullible to journey to the tree "and three times walk round my girth for all to see." But now in the twentieth century this journey is no longer necessary. For a small fee (in American money) the sick and the gullible can receive a sample piece of lucky cork its wonders to perform.

Surely the word "corker" stems from "cork." How otherwise account for Webster's definition and how unfortunate for Macbeth that he could not have consulted England's cork tree instead of the witches of evil omen!

A. L. F.

New York
March, 1941

CONTENTS

A SELECTED LIST OF REFERENCES

The available literature on cork is quite meager. In 1917, the Library of Congress at Washington issued a list of references on the cork industry and supplemented this with a second list dated May 11, 1936. Most of the references on these lists are to periodicals, and it is magazine articles that make up most of a cork bibliography in English. A number of these references in recent periodicals more or less generally available are listed below together with the few published books, including several in French and German of interest only to research students. A number of additional references will be found in text footnotes.

Blanchard, W. O. Cork Oak. *Journal of Geography*, October 1926, v. 25: 241-249.

Buttrick, P. L. The Romance of Cork. *American Forests*, March 1933, v. 39: 110-113.

Camus, A. *Les Chênes*. Paris, Paul Lechevalier & Fils, 1934. (For the botanist and forestry student; vol. VI of the author's Encyclopédie Economique de Sylviculture. French readers might also consult: Freixe, Emile. *Le Liège—Sa Culture, Son Commerce, Son Industrie*; Graffigny, Henry de. *Le Liège et Ses Applications* and Lamey, A. *Le Chêne-Liège—Sa Culture et Son Exploitation*.)

Cooke, G. B. Cork and Its Uses. *Journal of Chemical Education*, August 1931, v. 8: 1462-1492, and Cork and Cork Products in *The Crown*, November 1938—October 1939, v. 27, nos. 3-12 and v. 28, nos. 1-2, Baltimore, The Crown Cork and Seal Company.

Davis, B. Tree Bark with a Hundred Uses. *Scientific American*, November 1930, v. 143: 344-348.

Faubel, Arthur L. [Ed.] *Low Temperature Insulation*. New York, The Cork Institute of America, 1937 and 1940. (A testing report in two booklet-volumes of interest principally to engineering students.)

Müller, Eugen Anton. *Über die Korkeiche*. Vienna, R. Lechner, 1900. (Old, but has a good discussion on the history of the cork oak in Chapter IV.)

Origin of Cork Products. *Scientific American*, January 1928, v. 138: 48.

Stecher, Gilbert E. *Cork: Its Origin and Industrial Uses*. New York, D. Van Nostrand Company, 1914. (Out of print, but in many libraries.)

Thomas, P. Edwin. *Cork Insulation*. Chicago, Nickerson & Colins Company, 1928.

Woolsey, Theodore S., Jr. *French Forests and Forestry—Tunisia Algeria, Corsica*. New York, John Wiley & Sons, Inc. 1917.

Each of the various standard encyclopedias includes a short and, generally speaking, inadequate article on cork. Several of the larger American cork companies issue booklets and pamphlets which are among the best current cork publications. The Portuguese Junta Nacional da Cortica (Lisbon) publishes an excellent monthly *Boletim*, with an English section.

CHAPTER I

CORK AND THE CORK OAK

R ELATIVELY few people know the source of the everyday article—cork. One of the questions in a recent intelligence questionnaire was the following:

Turpentine is obtained from trees and cork comes chiefly from:
Ireland   *sea mollusks*
discarded artificial legs   *worn-out life preservers*
shallow surface mines   *trees*

Trees is the answer. Cork in all its forms comes from the bark of an oak tree known botanically as *Quercus Suber.*[1] For reasons which Nature alone controls, this oak tree grows in commercial stands only in areas bordering the Mediterranean Sea and all attempts to establish cork forests in this country and elsewhere have thus far been unsuccessful.

"Attempts were made as early as the year 1859 to introduce the cork oak into the United States, where the requirements of the tree, as regards temperature and rainfall, could be met over a wide range of territory, but none of these efforts were successful. Also in more recent years experiments have been carried out in southern California and Arizona, but, so far as known, no commercial cork has ever been produced on this side of the Atlantic. The Japanese have met with the same discouragement, and France has failed to produce results in Brittany and on the Atlantic islands, just off the coast."[2]

We now know that the use of cork goes back to the days of ancient Greece and Rome. Theophrastus (about 400 B.C.) refers to cork in his remarkable work on botany. Pliny mentions the use of cork for stoppers, floats and shoes; Horace, in Ode III, speaks

---

[1] A second species of cork oak—*Quercus Occidentalis*—is mentioned in some cork literature. *Quercus Occidentalis* (the western oak) is apparently slightly more hardy than *Quercus Suber* and was first differentiated from the latter in 1856 by the Swiss botanist, J. Gay. Modern authorities are now generally agreed that *Quercus Occidentalis* is a variety or sub species of *Quercus Suber*. Cf. the Camus volume mentioned in the list of references.

[2] Dun's *International Review*, March 1930. See also *Cork Insulation* by Pearl Edwin Thomas, pp. 4 and 5 and note Appendix D of this book, pp. 143-146, which reports on the latest developments in the California experiment mentioned in the above quotation.

of removing "the cork sealed with pitch from the wine vase"; Cato refers to cork in his famous *De Re Rustica,* Cap. 120, and Plutarch gives the following account of the use of cork by a messenger sent to Rome at a time when it was besieged by the Gauls:

"Pontius Cominius, having dressed himself in mean attire, under which he concealed some pieces of cork, could not pass the river by the bridge, therefore took off his clothes which he fastened upon his head, and having laid himself upon the pieces of cork swam over and reached the city."

These and many other similar references in the literature of classical antiquity indicate how common and widespread was the use of cork 2,000 and more years ago. In fact, the use of cork for floats and buoys was apparently so common among the Romans that the Latin expression *"nare sine cortice"* (literally, to swim without [the use of] cork) was used in a far more general idiomatic sense meaning "to need no [more] assistance."

During the 1780 decade, a German professor of economy at the University of Göttingen, Johann Beckmann, brought together practically everything that was then known about cork in an article in his *History of Inventions, Discoveries and Origins.*[1] Following an apology for including in a scientific treatise a discussion on so humble an article as cork, Beckmann justifies his discussion by describing the peculiar and remarkable physical properties of cork including especially its light weight and its imperviousness to penetration by liquids. Both of these properties, he wrote, are due to the infinite number of tiny pores in a piece of cork, which are "too small to afford a passage to the finest particles of water and wine." This porosity explanation of Beckmann's day will make an interesting comparison with the facts as we now know them and which we shall discuss shortly.

Beckmann then discusses the various uses made of cork and the historical development of these uses, noting that the Romans used cork for "as many purposes as at present." These uses, going back to Roman times, were (1) floats and buoys for nets and anchors,

---

[1] Beckmann's work was first published in German in installments during the years 1783 to 1788, and was later republished in a number of editions and translations. Two early nineteenth century books, each of which contained a summary of the then known facts about cork, deserve mention here. They are *A Dictionary, Practical, Theoretical and Historical, of Commerce and Commercial Navigation* by J. R. McCulloch, first published in 1832 in London, and *A Dictionary of Arts, Manufactures and Mines* by Andrew Ure, published in 1839 also in London.

(2) soles for sandals and shoes and (3) stoppers for jugs, vases and, later, bottles.[1]

CORK—COMPLETELY CELLULAR IN STRUCTURE

These simple uses of cork, which began with the ancients, continued with but little change down to almost the beginning of this

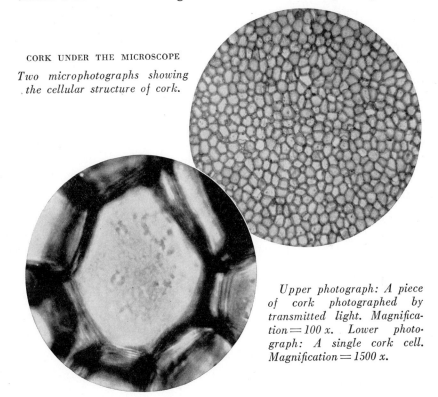

CORK UNDER THE MICROSCOPE

Two microphotographs showing the cellular structure of cork.

Upper photograph: A piece of cork photographed by transmitted light. Magnification = 100 x. Lower photograph: A single cork cell. Magnification = 1500 x.

century. But whether we are dealing with the simple uses of the ancients or the much more extensive and elaborate uses of cork in our own times, we find these uses all growing out of the outstanding character of cork—its cellular structure. This is the property which Beckmann called "porosity" and a knowledge of cork and

[1] In *Cork: Its Origin and Industrial Uses* by Gilbert E. Stecher (published in 1914), reference is made on page 39 to another use of cork by the ancients—its use by the early Egyptians in the construction of their coffins. Several Egyptologists with whom I consulted on this point have advised me that there is no evidence to support such a statement and that probably what some investigator took to be cork was instead certain of the embalming materials which had turned to a cork color and hardened.

an understanding of its many uses must begin with a study of the unique physical make-up of this oak-tree bark. The barks of most trees are made up in part of long fibers running lengthwise of the tree like the fine copper strands in an electric wire or cable. In contrast, the bark of the cork oak, which is the cork of commerce, is made up completely of myriads of tiny cells, each imprisoning within its walls a microscopic bit of air. Out of this distinctive characteristic of cork grow all its uses from simple floats and stoppers to modern insulation board and automobile gaskets.[1]

The illustrations on the preceding page show the cellular structure of cork. In a piece of natural cork only one cubic inch in size there are approximately 200,000,000 of these minute cells, averaging in their small diameter about $\frac{1}{1000}$ of an inch and each separated from the other by a thin, thread-like but remarkably strong membrane of resinous materials which binds the cells together. Slightly more than 50% of the volume of a piece of cork is accounted for by the captive air within the tiny cells.

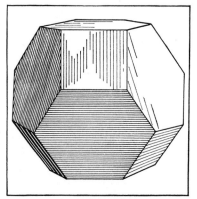

A TETRAKAIDECAHEDRON

The lower of the two illustrations on the preceding page, showing a single cork cell magnified 1,500 x, indicates a remarkable characteristic of the cells themselves; they are tetrakaidecahedral —14-sided. To the scientist this is another striking phenomenon with which Nature has endowed the bark of the cork oak. Years ago, the great English scientist, Lord Kelvin, established the fact that it takes 14-sided bodies or areas to solve the problem of dividing up space *without interstices* into uniform bodies of minimum surface dimensions. A piece of cork, in other words, is completely cellular with no "empty" spaces between the cells.[2]

[1] The bark of most trees contains cork cells but only in the cork oak are these cells in layers of sufficient thickness to be of commercial importance. Cf. *Commercial Timbers of the United States* by H. P. Brown and A. J. Panshin and a thesis by C. H. de Zeeuw, *Histology of Periderm Formation in Certain Northeastern Trees* in the library of the State College of Forestry, Syracuse, N. Y.

[2] Cf. *The Molecular Tactics of a Crystal* by Sir William Thomson (Lord Kelvin), Oxford University, The Clarendon Press, 1894 and Frederic T. Lewis in *Science*, December 21, 1928, pp. 625-626.

THE PHYSICAL PROPERTIES OF CORK

Virtually all of the physical properties of cork are based either directly or indirectly upon its unique cellular construction and it is these physical properties which account for the many and varied uses of cork and also for the existence of the far-flung cork industry. The most important of the physical properties of cork are the following:

1. Buoyancy—light weight
2. Compressibility
3. Resilience
4. Resistance to moisture and liquid penetration
5. Frictional quality
6. Low thermal conductivity
7. Ability to absorb vibration
8. Stability

1. *Buoyancy.* It was the light weight or buoyancy property of cork which accounted for its first known uses in the ancient world. With a specific gravity of approximately .25, cork is one of the lightest of all solid substances. Its buoyancy is, of course, the result of the fact, noted above, that more than 50% of the volume of a piece of cork is accounted for by the air imprisoned within the cells. This property of cork is the basis, either wholly or partially, for its use as buoys, life preservers and an almost endless variety of floats.

2. *Compressibility.* Industrially, this is one of cork's most important characteristics. A one-inch cube of cork has been compressed under pressures as great as 14,000 pounds per square inch without breaking and after the removal of the pressure the cube returned to 90% of its original one-inch height and showed no appreciable change in its length and breadth dimensions.[1] When cork is compressed apparently what happens is that some of the air trapped within the cells "escapes" but most of it remains trapped and is compressed *within the cells.* Therefore, when under compression cork does not spread or "flow" laterally to any appreciable extent. This characteristic of cork is shown by the photo-

[1] Cf. Giles B. Cooke, *Journal of Chemical Education,* August 1931, pp. 1462-1492.

graphs on this page, and it is this feature of cork which is the principal basis of the composition cork industry.

3. *Resilience.* This property of cork is the natural counterpart of its compressibility. Because pressure does not break down or destroy the tiny cell walls, but instead compresses the air within

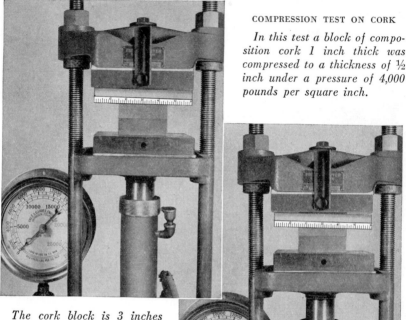

COMPRESSION TEST ON CORK

In this test a block of composition cork 1 inch thick was compressed to a thickness of ½ inch under a pressure of 4,000 pounds per square inch.

The cork block is 3 inches square and rests on a steel block the same size. Notice in the lower illustration the very slight amount of "bulge" at the ends which shows how little cork "flows" laterally when under pressure.

the cells, the moment the pressure is released the cork begins to spring back as the captive air within the cells returns to its normal pressure. Under ordinary conditions, cork does not harden or deteriorate, and no matter how long it is held under pressure it will take only a minimum of permanent "set." In addition to its importance to the composition cork industry, the resiliency of cork accounts largely for its use as stoppers and as a flooring material, both of which will be discussed in later chapters.

4. *Resistance to moisture and liquid penetration.* On this score the ordinary blotter is the complete opposite of the cork. Touch

[6]

an ink spot or any liquid with a blotter and the blotter immediately sucks up the liquid because the blotter is made up of tiny fibers which draw up the liquid by capillarity. While cork is not completely impervious to moisture penetration, its cellular structure gives it a high resistance to penetration by water and most other liquids, except strong alkalis, even when boiled in them. The photograph below shows how little nigrosine dye penetrated a cork block because of the high resistance of cork to liquid penetration and the filtering action of the tiny cork cells which kept out the dye. This property of cork accounts for its use in life preservers and as stoppers, buoys and floats.

A block of natural cork was boiled for twenty-four hours in an alcoholic solution of nigrosine dye. Left, before boiling. Center, after boiling. Right, cross section showing penetration of dye in pores only and not through cells.

5. *Frictional quality.* Cork is a highly frictional material. The coefficient of friction of cork is decidedly greater than that of rubber, leather and other materials often used for frictional purposes, and cork retains this frictional quality even when wet or coated with oil or grease. The illustrations on the next page show this striking characteristic of cork which again is due to its cellular structure. The exposed surface cells on the cork act like tiny suction cups and, as the photographs show, the cork block did not slide down the inclined plane until a 42° angle was reached whereas the leather block slid down at an 18° angle and the rubber block at 28°. Both natural cork and cork composition have this high frictional quality which will be discussed again from a product standpoint in the industry chapters.

6. *Low thermal conductivity.* Here is the physical property of cork which is the basis of the largest division of the cork industry. This most important physical property of cork will be discussed further in Chapter V, and therefore only a few words here on the principle involved. Next to a vacuum, a "dead" air space minutely

divided is one of the most efficient nonconductors of heat known to modern science. Cork, first coarsely ground and then baked in sheet form, is exactly such a nonconductor of heat and corkboard is today the standard insulation throughout the world for modern cold-storage rooms and chambers.

7. *Ability to absorb vibration.* Because of its inherent air-filled cellular character cork acts as a cushion and tends to absorb a part of any impact or vibration striking it. This is simple to see in the case of the vibration caused by a large ma-

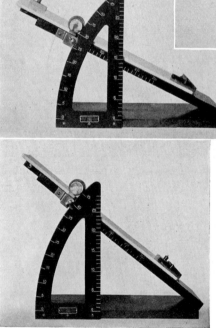

FRICTION TEST ON LEATHER, RUBBER AND CORK

The pieces of leather, rubber and cork used in this test were of identical contact surface and were weighted equally.

When the plane was inclined at an angle of 18°, the leather block slid down—upper photograph. At an angle of 28°, the rubber block slid down—middle photograph. Not until the inclined plane was at an angle of 42° did the cork block slide down—lower photograph.

For the practical significance of this test see the photograph on page 43.

chine; place a piece of cork between the bottom of the machine and the floor to which it is bolted and although the machine is standing on a solid—the cork—more than 50% of that "solid" is air. The machine in other words is standing on an "air cushion" —the cork—which absorbs most of the vibrations which would otherwise be communicated to the floor. Cork for this purpose is made in both block and sheet form and in various densities.

8. *Stability*. Cork is a tough, durable substance with a remarkable capacity for retaining its initial properties practically unimpaired wherever its use is recommended. Unlike many materials, it withstands progressive deterioration for a long time, and hence does not become less efficient until long after another material would be worn out. Temperature and humidity changes and similar atmospheric conditions have only slight effect on cork and its high degree of stability under varying conditions is another reason for its widespread use, particularly in the insulation and composition-cork fields.

THE CHEMISTRY OF CORK

So much for the physical properties of cork. As regards its chemical properties not nearly so much is known, even after 100 years of fairly continuous research during the last twenty-five of which the uses of cork have spread in industry and everyday life in forms virtually unknown at the beginning of the twentieth century. In 1839, Ure in his Dictionary summarized the results to date of the chemical research into the nature of cork in the following short paragraph:

"When cork is rasped into powder, and subjected to chemical solvents, such as alcohol &c., it leaves 70 per cent of an insoluble substance, called suberine. When it is treated with nitric acid, it yields the following remarkable products:—white fibrous matter 0.18, resin 14.72, oxalic acid 16.00, suberic acid (peculiar acid of cork) 14.4 in 100 parts."

The intervening century has of course added considerably to what was known of the chemistry of cork in Ure's day, but much still remains unknown and uncertain. We do know that, chemically, cork is decidedly inert, and except only as regards certain alkalies and strong solutions of some acids it is more resistant to chemical action than most natural products. Beyond this, however, what we know indicates the chemistry of cork to be very complicated. The following paragraphs are quoted from the chemical discussion in a recent article on cork:

"Very little is known concerning the chemical composition of cork. For over a hundred years chemists have been endeavoring to determine the nature of its constituents, but the literature is full of contradictions and the amount of definite information available is very limited.

There are also numerous contradictions in the literature in regard to the quantitative composition of cork. Age, growing conditions, quality of the cork, and the amount of absorbed moisture affect the results of quantitative work and no doubt account for some of the differences. G. Zemplin gives the following analysis of cork; the extractions were carried out in the order listed." [1]

Moisture	6.21	
Ash	4.12	(Mineral matter)
Alcohol extract	10.50	(Tannins, phlobaphenes, cerin, friedelin)
Alcohol KOH extract	32.50	(Fatty acids)
Water extract of residue	14.00	(Fatty acids)
Sulfuric acid (1.5%) extract	1.50	(Carbohydrates)
Lignocellulose	24.50	(Lignin, carbohydrates)
Residue resembling cellulose	4.17	(Cellulose, other carbohydrates)

Such are the physical and chemical characteristics and properties of the bark of the cork oak. On the basis of these characteristics and properties, plus one other, a great international industry has been built up. That other characteristic of cork is most important; it is the economic factor. Cork is reasonable in price. While not a "cheap" material it is not expensive and this is especially true when its life-cost is considered. With a moderate first cost, cork offers the economies due to its durability and stability. Long after substitute competitive materials have "set" or hardened or otherwise deteriorated this remarkable product of Nature remains live and resilient and continues to "carry on."

With this background, we turn to the industry built on cork and to the men and women who live by it. We shall begin with the raw material growing on trees—some of them as old or older than the United States—along the coast and back in the interior of Spain, Portugal, France, Italy, Morocco, Tunisia and Algeria.

[1] "Cork and Its Uses" by Giles B. Cooke in the *Journal of Chemical Education* for August 1931, pp. 1462-1492. Since Dr. Cooke's article was written there has been further research into the chemistry of cork of particular interest to advanced students. This concerns the so-called cork alcohols—cerin and friedelin. For an authoritative discussion covering this work see "Cerin and Friedelin" by Nathan L. Drake (and others) in the *Journal of the American Chemical Society* for September and October 1935 and September 1936, vol. 57, pp. 1570 and 1854, and vol. 58, pp. 1681 and 1684. See also a further discussion on "Cerin and Friedelin" by Nathan L. Drake and John K. Wolfe in the *Journal of the American Chemical Society* for November 1940, pp. 3018-3021 and "The Structure of Phellonic Acid" by Nathan L. Drake (and others) in the same publication for February 1941, pp. 617-620.

CHAPTER II

CORK WOOD—PRODUCTION AND MARKETING

FROM an area approximately the size of the State of New Jersey comes the world's cork supply. This area, estimated by various authorities as covering from 3,750,000 acres to 4,400,000 acres, stretches in a narrow belt for more than 1,000 miles along the northern coast of Africa and for more than 1,500 miles along the coast of Portugal, Spain and France. There is defi-

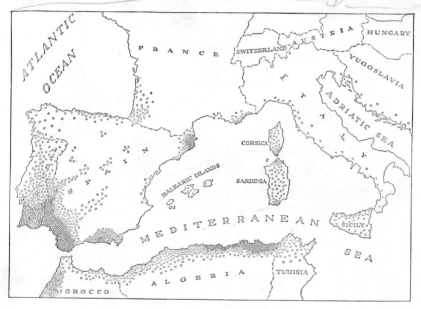

THE SOURCE OF THE WORLD'S CORK SUPPLY

Comparative density of the stands and forests is indicated by the tree symbol. The darkly shaded areas indicate dense growth and are the most important sources of supply.

nite evidence that cork oak trees once grew around the rim of the entire Mediterranean basin, but the ancient civilizations of Phenicia, Asia Minor and the Balkan Peninsula have left only traces of cork oak stands in the eastern Mediterranean territory. The outline map on this page shows the location and also the approximate density of the cork stands which at present produce an annual crop of from 250,000 to 300,000 tons of raw cork. About 70% of this total tonnage comes from Spain and Portugal, which together have only about half of the producing area. The following tabulation shows the approximate percentage of the total annual production coming from each of the important cork producing countries and also the approximate percentage of the total cork growing area included within each of these countries.[1]

	% of Production	% of Area
Portugal	35-40	25-30
Spain	28-32	15-20
France	4-5	5-7
Italy	2-3	4-5
Algeria	15-19	22-28
Morocco	4-5	13-16
Tunisia	2	5-7
Others	1	1

A cork tree that has never been stripped.

This tabulation shows that almost half of the cork producing area is located in northern and northwestern Africa, but these areas in Algeria, Morocco and Tunisia produce only approximately one-fourth of the total tonnage. The principal reason for this lies in the fact that in Africa the trees are not stripped as high up as they are in Spain and Portugal and the African yield per tree at each stripping is therefore considerably less than the European yield per tree. Furthermore, many of the cork stands in Africa are relatively young compared with those of Spain and Portugal. These newer Afri-

[1] Cf. W. O. Blanchard, *Journal of Geography*, October 1926, pp. 241-249. The figures in the table as it stands above represent the estimates of a number of authorities no two of whom agree. This is especially true of the area percentages. Some years the total strip may run 10 to 15% over 300,000 tons.

can stands are part of a cork forestation program sponsored by the French Government and are less than 50 years old. As these trees get older the yield from each will increase and the northern coast of Africa may become the world's most important cork producing area. The last frontiers of undeveloped cork areas are in this same section of northern Africa. Thousands of acres of cork producing lands have only recently been wrested from the control of native tribesmen and a program of development and commercial exploitation of these cork growing lands is now in progress.

A cork tree in Morocco that has been stripped up to the legal limit.

GROWTH AND LIFE OF THE CORK OAK

Much of the land on which the cork tree grows is two-crop land, the two principal crops being cork and pigs. The pigs root out the underbrush and are particularly fond of the cork oak acorns which ripen and fall to the ground. Also, in some sections of Spain and Portugal, it is not uncommon to find vineyards and other crops growing between cork trees where the stand is not very dense or concentrated.

Unlike our own oak trees, the cork oak is an evergreen. In appearance, the leaves resemble our holly leaves minus the sharp points and they are soft and velvety to the touch. Most of the trees when fully grown range from thirty to forty feet in height with trunks three to four feet in diameter but there are many old trees fifty feet or more in height and five feet through at the base. The cork oak on the average lives about 150 years although there are many growing trees 200 years old. Our cork of commerce is the outer bark of this tree which is periodically stripped from the trunk and in some areas from the larger of the lower limbs. The trees are first stripped when they are from twenty to thirty years of age and thereafter every nine or ten years during their pro-

Stripping the cork tree.

ductive life of approximately one hundred years. The governments of most of the cork-growing countries regulate by a law or legal regulation the size of the tree before its first stripping, the frequency of the strippings, the height of the trunk stripping and frequently the extent to which the branches may be stripped. Portuguese law, for example, requires that the bark may not be removed from cork trees until they have attained a circumference of 15½", and in Portugal the law prohibits the stripping of cork trees oftener than once every nine years.

The bark of the cork oak grows in two layers—an outer and an inner. The inner bark, or phellogen, is alive and acts as a base on which each year the tree adds a new inner layer to the cork. As these succeeding new inner layers are added to the living bark the outermost layers cease to be a living part of the tree and serve only as an insulating wrapper protecting the tree particularly against the hot desert winds known as siroccos, which frequently blow for days in the cork producing areas. Except in the case of only a few trees familiar to us, like the birch, if the bark is removed, or even cut through, the tree will die because the bark contains the vascular bundles that nourish the tree. But the outer bark of the cork oak, being only a protective layer, can be removed

Cork bark drying in the field.

from the tree without injuring it. This removal of the bark, known as "stripping," must be done very carefully and during the active growing season of the tree, for any injury to the inner living bark will prevent the formation of new cork and if the injury is serious the tree may die. The middle of the summer, from June through August, is the stripping period and stripping is seldom done while a sirocco is blowing because the heat of the wind would cause undue drying of the newly-exposed bark.

STRIPPING THE TREE

In the most common method of stripping two cuts are made around the tree with a sharp, two-bladed hatchet. One of these cuts is made at the ground level and the other at either the legal height limit or just below the main branches. These cuts are made clear through the outer bark and are then connected with two vertical cuts which usually follow natural crevices in the bark. The wedge-shaped hatchet handle is then inserted under the loosened bark and the whole sheet pried off in large and small pieces. Where the law permits it, the large lower branches, sometimes up to the third cross of the tree, are stripped in the same way. The bark from the branches is not so thick as from the trunk and is usually slightly lower in quality. The first stripping produces cork of a rough, grayish uneven surface, known in the United States as "virgin" cork and suitable only for grinding for cork insulation and cork composition products. The second stripping from a tree is considerably better than the first, but it is not until the third stripping that a tree begins to produce its finest quality of cork. About 40% of the cork produced by the second and subsequent strippings is of a low grade and is known in the trade as "refugo"; like virgin, this is suitable only for grinding purposes. The re-

[15]

Weighing cork on the Romana.

maining 60% is good wood suitable for the manufacture of all natural cork products such as bottle stoppers, floats, cork balls, polishing wheels and the like.[1]

After the bark is stripped from the trees it is piled up and left to dry for a few days, but before following it further we should consider its sale because much cork is sold while still on the trees. Cork varies so much as between the different growing areas and in different stands and forests within the same area that cork buying is a trade in itself.

"To buy intelligently then, the purchaser must not only know the production records of the forests but must also 'sample' each crop on which he bids. Through the forest in a bee-line, the buyer sends his 'sampler,' a picturesque worker with a big sack slung over his back and a tubular punch in his hand. As he goes he 'taps' every fifth or tenth or twentieth tree, removing a small cylindrical section of cork just as a fruit dealer plugs watermelons.

Dropped into the sampler's sack, these discs are taken back to the buyer's office for careful examination, and upon the judgment formed from an analysis of this cross-section a bid is made on the stripping of the forest.

In the privately owned lands of Spain and Portugal, the buyer deals directly with the owner or his agent. He may contract for an entire mountainside while the bark is still on the trees. In Morocco . . . and Tunisia, however, the French Government disposes of its cork wood at great public auctions. To these events, held at major centers in the cork growing regions of North Africa, come buyers and importers from all the important cork-using countries in the world.

While some sales in Northern Africa are conducted by bidding up the lots of cork, there also exists a method contrary to the auction custom that we know. Here the auctioneer does not ask for bids. He starts with a top price on each lot of cork to be sold. If his announcement is met with silence from his audience he names a slightly lower figure. Down he goes, shouting out successively lower figures until someone in his audience cries 'Je prends.' The first lot, usually a small one, is generally purchased by a small operator anxious to get the short quantity he needs before the larger buyers come in and take everything.

[1] It is well to understand that throughout the whole cork industry the term "wood" or "cork wood" refers only to the bark of the tree and never to the structural part of the tree which might be cut up into lumber. As a matter of fact, lumber made from the cork oak is so very dense, heavy and hard that it is but little used for building or woodworking. At times, especially when cork prices are low, old trees are cut down and made into charcoal.

Prices are called faster and faster by the auctioneer as he comes down to lower figures on each lot of cork. The successful buyer is he who can sit listening to descending figures without betraying by his facial expression the fact that soon he is going to say '*Je prends.*' (I take.)"[1]

WEIGHING, BOILING AND SORTING

Let us return now to the stripped cork we left drying in piles in the forests. After several days of drying the cork is weighed, usually on the *"Romana"* which is a type of simple scales dating back almost 2,000 years to the Romans. The cork is next taken to a boiling station, located centrally in the stand or forest or in a near-by town. After a further period of seasoning the cork is boiled in large vats. The boiling serves several purposes; it softens the cork and increases its elasticity so that it can be flattened out for baling; it softens the woody

A boiling station in the field.

outer layer of the bark which is scraped off and the boiling also removes much of the dirt and sap and some of the tannic acid in the bark, thereby reducing the weight for shipping. After the first rough sorting, the flattened pieces of cork "go to town"—some of them on the backs of burros, most of them in modern automobile trucks.

[1] *Cork—Its Origin and Uses*, Armstrong Cork Company, 1930. The auctions referred to are held during October-December of each year. The 1940 French-African auction schedule, for example, was as follows: Tunis, November 6; Constantine, November 28; Algiers, December 3; Oran, December 6, and Rabat, December 12.

A load of cork comes to town.

Seville in Spain is one of the most important cork centers in the world, and every year into this city pours the cork from the surrounding areas. Arriving at Seville, the cork goes either to the local factories or is prepared for shipment to foreign countries. If the latter, the crude bales put together at the boiling stations are opened up, the rough edges are trimmed, the cork is again sorted for quality, this time into thirty or more different grades and then baled for shipment. Each bale weighs from 140 to 180 pounds and is made up with large slabs on top and bottom and bound together with iron straps.

The standard international unit of weight used in the cork trade is the metric ton (1,000 kilos—2,204.6 pounds), but almost each of the principal growing regions has its own unit of weight with which cork buyers must be familiar. Some of the more important of these local units and their equivalents are:

Quintal metric—100 kilos—220.46 pounds—Africa and Italy
Quintal Catalan—41.50 kilos—91.49 pounds—Cataluna
Quintal Castillano—46.01 kilos—101.43 pounds—Southern Spain (arroba also used)
Quintal Provincial—80 kilos—176.37 pounds—Southeastern France (metric quintal also used)
Quintal Gascon—50 kilos—110.32 pounds—Southwestern France (metric quintal also used)
Arroba cork—15 kilos—33.07 pounds—Portugal and Southwestern Spain

Four foreign countries, the United States, Great Britain, France and Germany, regularly take approximately 85% of the world's annual production of cork. Approximately 40% of each year's total stripping comes to the United States. From this point on it will be the American share which interests us.

Cork coming to the United States is shipped from many ports, but the most important are Lisbon, Oporto, Seville, Algeciras, Casablanca, Djidjelli, Bone, Faro, Sines and Algiers. Small lots of up to 500 or possibly 1,000 tons are loaded in general cargo steam-

Trimming the edges.

ers of French, Spanish, Italian and American lines maintaining more or less regular sailings between Mediterranean ports and the north Atlantic seaboard. A good deal of cork is brought over in full cargoes of 1,800 to 2,500 tons each loaded in tramp steamers, chartered for certain specified westward crossings. Gloucester City, New Jersey, is the principal port of entry for cork into the United States although large tonnages are handled at Philadelphia, Wilmington, New York and Baltimore, while occasional small shipments come in through such ports as Houston, Texas, Detroit and San Francisco.

At the end of Chapter I we referred to the fact that cork while not a "cheap" material is not expensive. The standard pricing unit for cork wood which comes to this country is the hundred-weight, and the different grades vary considerably in price. The following tabulation

Scraping and baling. The primitive baling press shown in this picture has been replaced at many stations by a modern hydraulic press.

Cork wood baled for shipment to America.
Weight varies from 140 to 180 pounds.

shows the average yearly dollar prices for four qualities of Portuguese cork wood and for grinding cork for the years listed. This tabulation, which is intended only to indicate the approximate market value of cork wood of different grades and of grinding cork, shows the average prices for the past eight years of these different grades of cork, per cwt. or per ton, delivered at Philadelphia and takes into consideration the fluctuations in the foreign currencies in which the shippers are paid.

CORK WOOD AND GRINDING CORK—AVERAGE PRICES—1932-1940

[*Prices c.i.f. Philadelphia. Wood, per cwt. Grinding cork, per long ton.*]

| | Corkwood—Qualities | | | | Grinding |
	1st	2nd	3rd	4th	Cork
1933	$20.18	$12.75	$ 6.74	$3.96	$26.69
1934	29.19	19.24	9.75	5.13	37.85
1935	28.28	18.91	9.47	5.16	36.16
1936	29.45	20.68	11.24	5.93	36.48
1937	27.81	19.95	11.35	6.34	52.13
1938	19.90	15.06	8.50	5.23	43.31
1939	22.09	15.44	9.33	5.82	35.38
1940	23.77	16.69	9.27	6.00	46.42

A cork stand in Estremadura.

CORK WOOD—PRODUCTION AND MARKETING

Raw cork enters this country duty free and is divided for statistical purposes by the customs authorities into two classifications —cork wood and cork waste. The former is the bales of cork wood we described above while the latter comes from the baling stations and foreign factories. Waste is perfectly good cork; in fact it may be waste of the finest quality wood from which champagne corks have been cut, but in pieces too small for anything but grinding. On page 22 you will find a statistical tabulation showing the imports into the United States of cork wood and cork waste both in terms of pounds and value from 1900 through 1940.[1]

Because every pound of cork used by the United States must be imported and because of the importance of many cork products from a national defense standpoint cork has been classified as a "critical material" by the Army and Navy Munitions Board at Washington. A brief discussion of this will be found in Appendix C, pp. 141-142.

[1] This table has been prepared from the import statistics of cork wood and cork waste as reported by the United States Department of Commerce. The Government's import classification does not agree with practice and usage in the cork industry in that virgin cork and some of the refugo imports are classified and included in the Government's statistics as cork wood. While virgin and refugo are cork wood they are suitable only for grinding and therefore so far as the cork industry is concerned are always regarded as cork waste. [Postscript: Beginning as of January 1941, the Government changed its raw cork import classifications so that virgin cork (previously included in "Cork Wood") is now classified as "Cork Waste"—as it should be.]

Unloading cork from Portugal opposite Philadelphia.

CORK AND THE AMERICAN CORK INDUSTRY

IMPORTS OF CORK WOOD AND CORK WASTE 1900-1940

[Through 1917, data are for fiscal years, July 1 to June 30. Subsequent years are on calendar basis, January 1 to December 31]

UNMANUFACTURED CORK

	Pounds	Dollars
1900		1,446,423
1901	Pounds	1,727,921
1902	figures	1,815,723
1903	not	1,737,366
1904	reported	1,484,405
1905	prior	1,728,743
	to	
1906	1908.	1,837,354
1907		2,358,873
1908	60,664,316	2,092,732
1909	78,330,391	2,016,534
1910	109,271,575	3,152,280
1911	139,602,251	4,286,760
1912	118,432,309	3,247,086
1913	133,227,878	3,152,070

	CORK WOOD		CORK WASTE	
	Pounds	Dollars	Pounds	Dollars
1914	88,282,529	2,646,018	90,487,964	1,205,776
1915	24,897,803	1,420,581	96,575,427	1,334,262
1916	32,866,700	1,517,366	122,577,224	1,617,518
1917	40,273,005	2,125,633	120,677,624	1,743,184
1918	22,560,059	1,297,636	72,421,740	1,233,009
1919	28,286,942	1,802,506	131,641,699	2,558,556
1920	53,927,976	2,596,600	169,549,364	3,741,730
1921	22,147,868	959,947	88,255,141	1,397,212
1922	60,116,486	1,560,059	184,541,464	2,484,321
1923	62,975,549	1,776,417	164,571,128	1,951,143
1924	61,556,348	1,234,424	131,048,779	1,377,714
1925	76,430,087	1,454,050	137,229,147	1,540,804
1926	126,354,512	2,908,754	179,347,201	2,731,953
1927	124,000,952	3,063,026	99,089,741	2,312,257
1928	87,797,993	3,067,130	141,872,730	3,141,463
1929	90,642,124	3,239,632	176,955,502	4,988,851
1930	74,820,237	2,626,931	99,794,298	2,870,662
1931	55,518,712	1,618,949	79,881,940	1,394,210
1932	29,599,399	684,349	88,838,146	1,172,323
1933	93,931,668	1,698,374	93,252,117	1,156,571
1934	66,111,435	2,287,084	56,453,104	1,025,197
1935	70,448,230	1,747,188	82,627,329	1,310,219
1936	74,859,909	2,353,505	141,530,400	2,226,566
1937	115,448,197	3,819,601	207,449,497	4,696,014
1938	48,383,343	1,345,911	109,998,037	1,997,879
1939	63,403,483	1,566,416	164,171,282	2,524,050
1940	107,403,453	2,618,443	210,932,600	3,683,839

CHAPTER III

THE AMERICAN CORK INDUSTRY

ONE William King has generally been regarded as the founder of the American cork industry. Actually, however, it was William King's father, Stephen, who, about the year 1830, started cork manufacturing in this country with the opening of a small factory on Water Street in New York City.[1] The United States decennial census of 1850 is the first such census to report the existence of an American cork manufacturing industry. As of 1849, this census reports a total of 14 cork manufacturing establishments in operation, employing altogether 104 workers and a total investment of $43,000. The output, made up entirely of cork stoppers, was valued at $139,000.

The start was a solid one and the new American industry began a steady growth despite the fact that the industry's products for its first fifty years were made up entirely of cork stoppers and a few natural cork specialties such as cork floats and buoys. Twenty years after the census of 1850 made first reference to the industry, the number of plants had doubled while the number of workers had increased from 104 to 482. These and the other statistical details reported by each decennial census from 1870 to 1900 are shown in the following summary table.

	1869	1879	1889	1899
Number of Establishments	27	46	65	62
Number of Wage Earners	482	792	2,019	2,340
Wages Paid	$145,000	$ 233,000	$ 637,000	$ 688,000
Cost of Materials	427,000	976,000	1,502,000	2,404,000
Value Added by Manufacture....	328,000	591,000	1,338,000	1,988,000
Value of Product	755,000	1,567,000	2,840,000	4,392,000
Capital Invested	347,000	872,000	1,869,000	2,684,000

Until the last few years of this period, the industry remained what it was at the start—a cork-cutting industry. This term frequently appears in the old records and is, of course, accounted for by the fact that the products continued to be cork stoppers and other natural cork products cut out of the cork wood.

---

[1] Cf. addendum to this chapter, Appendix E, pp. 147-148.

THE INDUSTRY EXPANDS—INSULATION AND CORK TILE

During the last decade of the nineteenth century, however, it became increasingly evident that there were possibilities in this oak tree bark beyond its use as stoppers and floats. The insulating properties of cork had long been recognized in a commonly accepted way. The ancient Romans used slabs of cork bark in the construction of beehives undoubtedly, in part, because of the insulating property of cork. Spanish and Portuguese peasant farmers used thin sheets of cork bark as wall and floor coverings to keep some of the heat of summer and cold of winter out of their meager homes. During the stripping season the workers build shelter huts of cork bark. From the very beginning the cork tree had tried to call man's attention to the insulating properties of its bark by the way in which it withstood the burning siroccos. These hot desert winds frequently blow for days and weeks in the cork growing areas, killing or scorching the less hardy plants and trees. The cork oaks, however, show little or no effects from even the most withering sirocco due to the highly efficient insulating wrapper of bark with which each tree is covered.

It was not until about 1890, however, that the commercial possibilities of cork as an insulating material began to be developed. The first of these developments occurred in Europe. About 1890, a German firm brought out an "impregnated" corkboard for insulation purposes. This corkboard was made of granulated cork and a binder, and its development marks the beginning of the ex-

A ton of cork goes ashore.

pansion of the cork industry which started at the end of the last century and which has continued to the present time.

Impregnated corkboard never became an important product of the industry because of one of those discoveries which so often change the whole course of an industrial development. This accidental discovery will be covered more fully later in Chapter V on insulation; it will be sufficient here to note only that in October 1892, an American by the name of John T. Smith patented a process for the manufacture of corkboard insulation without the use of a binder. In a relatively few years, this new-process, American corkboard superseded the older German board and the manufacture of insulation corkboard was soon on a scale which made the cork industry no longer a simple cork-cutting trade.

During the same years which saw the development of cork insulation, efforts were being made in this country to perfect a cork flooring material. About 1900, these efforts resulted in the manufacture of cork floor tile on a commercial basis. While this product has not become as important as insulation corkboard and some other cork products, its development is of signficance to us here as another extension of the cork industry beyond the limits of a simple cork-cutting trade.

And things were happening in the old cork-cutting trade. Machines were replacing hand operations and automatic machinery was taking the place of simpler machines in the manufacture of cork stoppers. Also, natural cork products were being made in an increasing variety of sizes and shapes and for a multitude of new

[25]

From ocean freighter to barge.

uses that ranged from baseball centers and policemen's whistles to carburetor floats and polishing wheels. Each of these new products and uses further extended the limits of the old American cork-cutting business that William King had founded shortly before 1850. And each of these new developments called for an increasing volume of raw cork so that, as the table on page 22 shows, the imports of raw cork in 1910 were double the imports of ten years earlier—and that was only the beginning of the increase.

COMPOSITION CORK IS DEVELOPED

The possible uses of natural cork are somewhat restricted by the variability of the material in its natural state and due too to

its availability only in pieces that are irregular in size, thickness and shape. Partly because of these inherent limitations in natural cork, during the 1890's the industry went to work on the development of a manufactured cork product which would meet the demand for a live, resilient material that would remain live and that would not break down in contact with oil and grease. The development of the new

Cork as it comes from the tree. The piece on the left is virgin cork.

product was slow despite an increasing demand for such a material—a demand which was greatly aggravated, beginning about 1905-1906 with the conversion of the automobile industry to a mass production industry. Finally, after some fifteen years of research and experimentation the new product—composition cork [1]—was perfected. The new product was the complete answer to industry's problem of a long-lived, resilient material and one which would stand up in constant contact with petroleum products.

[1] Sometimes called "artificial cork" and so it is in the literal meaning, "produced by art or skill," but not in the sense of "not genuine or real" because it is completely and wholly ground-up natural cork plus only a binder.

A full description of this material, its development and uses will come later; here its significance is that by 1910 it had been developed and was in commercial production. It completed the present diversified-product character of the American cork industry which was now ready for the demands made upon it by the Great War and the expansion

The block of natural cork in the upper photograph was cut from the natural wood as marked in the lower photograph.

which took place during the succeeding twenty years. The statistical tabulation on page 23 showing the growth of the industry down to 1900 stops with the census report for 1899. The following tabulation continues this statistical "picture" of the American cork industry for the years indicated down to 1939, the latest year for which these data are available.[1]

	1909	1919	1929	1935	1939
Number of Establishments	62	62	35	34	35
Number of Wage Earners	3,142	3,545	3,842	3,370	3,265
Wages Paid	$1,098,000	$ 3,387,000	$ 4,209,000	$ 3,511,000	$ 3,933,000
Cost of Materials..	3,435,000	9,135,000	12,603,000	7,267,600	8,412,000
Value Added by Manufacture ...	2,505,000	7,147,000	10,421,000	6,719,000	9,311,000
Value of Product..	5,940,000	16,282,000	23,023,000	13,986,600	17,723,000
Capital Invested ..	5,327,000	14,570,000	[Report Discontinued]		

[1] Beginning with 1904 the census of manufactures data are available for every five-year period until 1919 when they are published for every other year, *i.e.*, 1921, 1923, 1925, etc. See the separate volumes of the United States Census of Manufactures.

RECENT TRENDS AND DEVELOPMENTS

Several interesting developments in the industry are revealed by this tabulation in addition to the record of growth and expansion shown. Between 1919 and 1929, the number of separate companies was cut almost in half. The two most important reasons for this shrinkage are failures and consolidations. The ten years between 1919 and 1929 brought prohibition to the United States and these same ten years saw the beginning on a significant scale of the substitution of various kinds of patented bottle closures for the old cork stopper. Both of these developments, coupled with the post-war liquidation which went on throughout all industry, were too much for a number of small cork-stopper manufacturers who simply disappeared from the business. This same ten-year period was enormously fruitful of consolidations and mergers in all lines of American industry, and the cork industry did not es-

Making tapered cork stoppers in 1900.
[Compare with the photograph on page 38]

cape this movement, although it was by no means as extensive as in other lines. It nevertheless helped reduce the number of establishments in 1929 as compared with 1919 as shown in the tabulation on the preceding page while all the other figures show substantial increases.

A second striking feature brought out by the tabulation is the "toll" taken of the cork industry by the economic collapse of 1929. This is apparent from a comparison of the 1935 data with those for 1929. It is even more evident by a comparison of the data for an intervening year like 1933 for by 1935 the industry was coming back. In 1933, for example, the number of wage earners had dropped to 2,634 and the value of product to $11,200,000, the latter figure being less than half the 1929 value.

Cork stopper manufacturing in 1900—sorting and grading.

As American industries go the cork manufacturing industry is fairly well concentrated in this country. With only a few exceptions the plants are located in Atlantic seaboard States. There is, of course, a rather obvious reason for this concentration: the raw cork all has to be imported and it is therefore most economical, as a rule, to manufacture it as near the port of entry as possible and then to ship the finished products throughout the country. Most of the manufacturing plants are therefore located in New York, New Jersey, Pennsylvania, Delaware and Maryland. There are two plants in Detroit, where they have the advantage of being next door to many of the large automobile plants, and there are also two plants in Chicago. By far the largest number of plants, although not the largest plants in size, is located in or around New York City where the shipping facilities both for incoming cork wood and outgoing cork products are second to none.

[29]

THE SEASONAL UPS AND DOWNS

In common with most other mass production industries the cork industry shows decided seasonal variations. The various products are so different and are sold to such different classes of trade that a study showing the seasonal variations in the industry as a whole is not at all indicative. In the stopper division of the cork industry the seasonal variation is so very erratic that it is possible only to say for this division that the sales of cork stoppers reach a low point for the year in the spring and climb to their yearly high in the fall of the year, usually October or November. The repeal of prohibition has helped make the seasonal swings in the sales of cork stoppers somewhat less pronounced than they were during the so-called "dry" years.

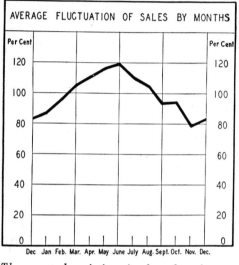

AVERAGE FLUCTUATION OF SALES BY MONTHS

The seasonal variations in the sales of composition cork products.

The seasonal variation in the composition cork division of the industry is considerably more uniform from year to year. The chart above shows these seasonal ups and downs in this division within the year. From this it will be noted that the yearly high point comes in June where the seasonal index stands at 120 and then the sales drop off to the end of the year to a relative figure of approximately 80% of the yearly average.

As might be expected, the insulation corkboard industry, being closely allied with the building industry, shows a pronounced seasonal variation which corresponds quite closely with the seasonal variation in the building industry. The chart opposite showing the variation in the corkboard sales by months indicates that the sales climb to a high in the spring of the year and then drop rather steadily to a low at the beginning of the winter season when building operations have to be curtailed. The chart indicates that the variation between the high and the low in the yearly sales of insulation corkboard is from approximately 80 to about 130.

Cork products can be manufactured and stored in warehouses for almost indefinite periods with no deterioration whatsoever and in order to reduce the evil effects of the seasonal swings in the sales of cork products upon the employment of workers in the industry, most of the manufacturers, including particularly the larger ones, manufacture for stock during the "slower" selling seasons. By doing this the manufacturers are able to stabilize employment throughout the year at fairly constant figures thereby avoiding the evils of overtime during part of the year and layoffs and shutdowns during other periods.

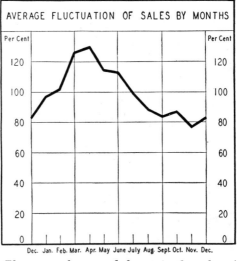

The seasonal ups and downs in the sales of corkboard insulation.

The American cork industry was among the first of the industries to draw up a code of fair competition under the NRA law passed in June, 1933. The cork industry's code (No. 199) was approved on January 12, 1934, but the industry had voluntarily made the labor provisions of its code effective five months before the code was officially approved by the Government. At a meeting in New York City on August 3, 1933, attended by practically all the manufacturers in the business, the industry's code of fair competition was approved and it was agreed by all the manufacturers to put the labor provisions into effect as of August 14, 1933.

THE MARKETING OF CORK PRODUCTS

It is frequently said that the cork industry taken as a whole includes practically every legal marketing plan. This is due to the great diversity of the industry's products and to the widespread differences in the types of buyers to whom the cork industry sells its products. In the case of most of these products, only a relatively small percentage is sold directly to the ultimate users most of whom are never conscious of the extent to which they buy and use cork.

Cork insulation products are sold to builders and contractors principally. Cork composition products are sold to bottlers, machinery and automobile manufacturers and the like. Cork stoppers are sold overwhelmingly to bottlers of various liquid products; occasionally a housewife may buy a handful of corks in a 5-and-10-cent store or in a hardware store but she is much more likely to save the corks which come in the bottled goods she buys. Cork tile is sold to builders and flooring contractors who install it in the buildings they are constructing. The great bulk of cork marine goods is sold to steamship and ferry companies and boat builders. And so it goes throughout the long list of manufactured cork products.[1] Although seemingly endless in variety this list of products can be grouped into five major product classifications depending upon the type of cork used or the service for which the product is intended. These five major product classifications are:

1. Cork stoppers and natural cork specialties
2. Cork insulation products
3. Cork composition and composition products
4. Cork tile
5. Cork marine goods

The chapters of this book which follow will describe each of these classes of products separately. A brief account of the manufacturing process in each case will be included; this will be followed by a short discussion of the principal uses of the various materials and of the marketing plan under which each type of product is sold.

At the end of Chapter II we had our raw material transported from the growing areas over to this country. It had already been sorted twice—once, very roughly, back in the hills at the boiling stations, and a second time at the baling stations. This second sorting resulted in a classification of some 30 grades. But this is wholly inadequate. Delivered at the American factory, the cork wood is again sorted and classified according to quality and thickness and a shipment of wood which contained 30-odd classifica-

[1] In Appendix A, beginning on page 121, will be found a descriptive listing of cork products according to use and principal type of service.

tions upon arrival in this country will often be "broken" into from 100 to 150 grades before it starts moving through a manufacturing plant. The difference between many of these numerous grades

Cork wood—final sorting at an American plant.

is usually so slight that an inexperienced observer would see none at all, but on the judgment of the experienced sorters who make this last grading may depend the difference between profit and loss on the whole manufacturing operation. In no branch of the industry is this final sorting of more importance than in the stopper division with which our industry chapters begin.

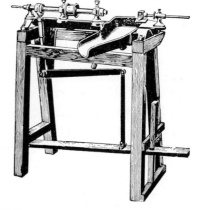

A FOOT BLOCKER

This is one of the "basic" machines in cork stopper manufacturing. See the description on page 38 and compare with the automatic blocker shown on page 37.

CHAPTER IV

CORK STOPPERS AND NATURAL CORK
SPECIALTIES

B Y far the oldest branch of the cork industry and the one with which the American industry started, the stopper division is today still one of the three most important. While the importance of this division has declined somewhat during the past ten years for reasons which will be discussed later in this chapter, the use of cork stoppers in this country alone still runs into the hundreds of millions annually.

We have already noted that the use of cork as a stopper goes back to the period of ancient Rome, but from what we know of them the cork stoppers of the ancients were very crude things and were generally used in connection with pitch or a sticky substance to make a good seal. The cork stopper as we know it today comes from the late Middle Ages rather than directly from ancient Rome. Most authorities agree that the cork stopper came into common use contemporaneously with the glass bottle but as to just when the glass bottle became a common article of widespread use there is some disagreement. The *Encyclopedia Americana* says, "The use of cork for stopping glass bottles is generally considered to have been introduced about the fifteenth century," and Beckmann, in his *History,* agrees with this. He says:

"Stoppers of cork seem to have been first introduced after the invention of glass bottles, and of these I find no mention before the fifteenth century."

Apparently, the widespread use of a more or less modern cork stopper came rather slowly for, according to Beckmann, it was not until the end of the seventeenth century that the apothecaries in Germany began to use cork stoppers to replace the old, more expensive wax stopper. For our purposes here it will be sufficient to note simply that the use of cork stoppers as bottle closures goes back about 500 years.

As is the case with all cork products the use of cork for stoppers is directly attributable to the cellular character of the bark of the cork oak. Among the principal physical properties of cork discussed in Chapter I are four such properties which make cork an ideal closure material. These four properties are its compressibility, resilience, resistance to moisture and liquid penetration and stability. Due to its compressibility and resilience, a cork stopper

NINE DIFFERENT TYPES
OF CORK STOPPERS

Top row:

   Wine cork
   Shell cork
   Champagne cork

Center row:

   Wedge-top cork
   Flange cork
   Tapered cork
   Dome-top cork

Bottom row:

   Orifice reducer
   "Specie" or jar cork

somewhat larger in diameter than the inside diameter of a bottle neck can be pushed into the bottle and, once in, its tendency to expand back to its original size causes it to grip the bottle neck with a friction hold so tight as to give a practically perfect seal. An outstanding advantage of this friction seal is that it extends over a wide area inside the bottle neck. A #10 straight cork, for example, 1 inch in diameter and $1\frac{1}{2}$ inches long furnishes a sealing area of over $3\frac{1}{2}$ square inches.

Because of cork's resistance to moisture and liquid penetration, a good stopper of the proper size acts as a very effective barrier to even the slightest leaking or seepage of the liquid within the bottle while, because of the stability of cork and its refusal to

[35]

take a "set," a cork stopper retains its compressibility and resilience almost indefinitely. Further, because of the chemical inertness of cork it can be used as a closure material for all liquids except a few alkalies, like ammonia, and some very destructive acids, like nitric and sulphuric.

The cork stoppers made today are of two principal types—"straights" and "tapers." The former are straight-sided cork cylinders used largely for the bottling of wine. Tapered corks are made with one end larger than the other and are used principally in the bottling of medicines, extracts and similar liquids. These two basic types of stoppers are made in a number of different variations as will be seen from the illustration on the preceding page showing the principal kinds of cork stoppers made today. In diameter, cork stoppers vary from size 000 ($\frac{1}{4}''$) to stoppers 6 inches in diameter. Most sizes come in three different lengths designated as short, regular and extra long; some sizes of tapered corks are also made in an extra extra long length. Being essentially a product of Nature, even after completely manufactured, cork stoppers vary greatly in quality as will be described later.

THE INDUSTRY BEGINS IN SPAIN

Stopper manufacturing as an industry appeared first about the middle of the eighteenth century as a distinctly local, hand craft in and around the town of Llacostera in the Province of Gerona, Spain. At first, cork stoppers were made entirely by hand and

Cork stopper manufacturing—fillet slicing.

there are still some handmade corks manufactured in Europe. The manufacturing was very simple and consisted first of cutting the bark into narrow strips which were then subdivided into small squares

This picture shows how cork stoppers are punched from the sliced fillets across the grain of the wood. The punched fillets are blocker waste—a valuable and useful by-product.

and these were rounded by turning them around on a very sharp knife. A good workman could turn out only from 2,000 to 2,500 handmade corks per day and the days were long.

Once established, the industry did not continue long on an entirely handmade basis. Early in the nineteenth century, according to Ure's *Dictionary*, one Sarah Thompson was granted a patent in England on a machine to be driven by hand, steam, horse or other power for the manufacture of cork stoppers from the original cutting of the wood to the final rounding operation. The manufacturing of stoppers as carried on today in a modern factory is done entirely by machinery some of which is completely automatic, but it is interesting to note that the process of manufacturing by first cutting out squares which are later rounded is still in

[37]

Cork stopper manufacturing—an automatic blocker at work.

use. In a modern manufacturing plant, however, the bulk of the stoppers is produced by "punching" the cork cylinders directly from the wood without first cutting out squares. This process is known as "blocking" and is done either by hand or on automatic blocking machines. Two or three interesting operations precede blocking; let us go back to them.

HOW CORK STOPPERS ARE MADE

We begin with the graded cork wood as described at the end of Chapter III. The sorted slabs start in a steam box in which live steam softens the wood, increases its bulk slightly and makes it pliable and workable. After steaming, the slabs are cut on a circular-knife machine into fillets or narrow strips equal in *width* to the *length* of the stopper to be cut because stoppers (except the large specie or jar corks for which there is only a limited demand) are cut *across* the grain (pores) of the wood and not *with* the grain. The photograph of a punched fillet shown on the preceding page tells most of the story in the manufacture of stoppers.

The cut strips now go to the blockers referred to earlier. A hand blocking machine looks very much like a simple woodworking lathe except that in the blocker the cutting knife revolves and is "pushed" against the block of cork wood by a lever mechanism operated by a treadle. An automatic blocker is shown in the photograph on the preceding page. Whether punched out by hand

[38]   *A battery of automatic tapering machines in a modern cork stopper factory. Compare with the photograph on page 28.*

or on the automatic blocker the product is the same—natural cork cylinders varying in size from those for tiny perfume vials to stoppers six inches in diameter for big jars and jugs.

Sorting finished cork stoppers.

We now have our stoppers in a semi-finished condition if we are making "straights" such as are used in wine bottles. Many stoppers are tapered and if we are making these, our straight-sided stoppers go to the tapering machines in which, one at a time, the little cork cylinders are held up, at the proper angle, against a large knife in a horizontal position which slices a thin shaving off each cork, thereby making the taper. The stoppers, both straights and tapers, are next washed, bleached and sterilized in a chemical bath. They are then dried in large centrifugal driers, and some of them go through other processes, such as branding with a name or trade-mark, paraffining or special shaping.

Next comes the all-important process of sorting. Even though the wood was very elaborately and thoroughly graded, the finished stoppers vary greatly and must be sorted for quality. Cork sorters are highly skilled operators, usually women, the best of whom can sort about 35,000 corks in a day. They examine the corks as they come in large baskets from the driers and in the flash of an eye determine the grade of each cork in a run. The American industry generally uses the following basic grading classification which individual manufacturers vary to suit their own requirements:

TAPERED CORKS	STRAIGHT CORKS	WINE CORKS
Extra Select	A Quality	Extra Firsts
A Quality	B Quality	Firsts
Select	B² Quality	Extra Seconds
B Quality	C Quality	Seconds
XXXX	D Quality	Extra Thirds
Commercial XXXX	E Quality	Thirds
C Quality		Extra Fourths
XXX	SPECIE OR JAR CORKS	Fourths
XX	X X X	Fifths
X	X X	
Common	X	

Some of the very large corks manufactured by the industry are laminated: that is, they are made of two or more pieces of wood because of the difficulty of getting wood of high quality that is sufficiently thick. The separate pieces of wood are glued together with an insoluble glue and the corks are then punched out in the usual manner. These laminated or glued corks are made in three grades—(1) regular, (2) fine and (3) extra fine.[1] A small quantity of specie or jar corks is manufactured by punching through the thickness of the cork wood, which means that this type of stopper is cut *with* the grain or pores of the wood and is therefore a very flat cork ranging in thickness from ½″ to ¾″.

THE COMPETITIVE PROBLEM—CORK STOPPERS *vs.* THE FIELD

Until fairly recently, cork stoppers were finished products ready for market after they were washed and graded. During recent years, however, an increasing volume of American-made stoppers is being attached to tops of various kinds—wood, molded phenolic compounds and various metals. These topped stoppers meet a real need for purposes where plain corks and screw caps are not wholly satisfactory; these topped stoppers are definitely part of the competitive problem which has developed in the stopper industry during the past ten or twelve years—the economic problem of competition between cork stoppers and other forms of closures. This problem is not a new one, nor is it at all peculiar to the manufacture and sale of cork stoppers. On the contrary, it is the problem which all long-lived industries meet sooner or later.

[1] Cork stoppers are also made of composition cork. These will be referred to in a later industry chapter.

Even before the stopper industry was founded in this country it ran into this problem of competitive substitution. Beckmann concluded the article on Cork in his *History* with a distinctly enthusiastic account of caoutchouc (India rubber) as a substitute material for cork in the manufacture of stoppers. Cork won out in that competition, but in other instances, the cork stopper was replaced by the substitute and made good its lost market by the opening up of a new closure field. The late Charles D. Armstrong (1861-1936), identified with the American cork industry for almost fifty years, in an address in Pittsburgh in 1927, summarized the ups and downs of the American cork industry almost from its beginning in this country as follows:

"When the cork business was started, stoppers for fruit jars were the important part of the business. With the coming of the Mason jar, the demand for the old-style corks diminished and in time disappeared. In the late 60's and during the 70's, the soft drink business developed rapidly and the demand for soda corks was very great, especially during the summer months. The invention of the spring stopper marked the beginning of the decline of the soda cork business. A soda bottle with a cork stopper is now never seen.

In the early 80's, great impetus was given to the bottling of beer by the use of the pasteurizing process. This gave rise to a large demand for corks of good quality, and the great brewers were by far the largest customers of the cork makers. Every keg of beer also carried a large tap cork. The invention of the crown cork marked the beginning of the decay

A modern cork stopper attached to a top made of synthetic phenolic resin.

of this business, and the old-style keg corks also disappeared, being superseded by the wooden tap bung which answers the same purpose better than cork and can be bought for a fraction of the price."

The tap cork, incidentally, has "come back" into fairly widespread use since Mr. Armstrong's remarks in 1927, but a substitution not of enough significance to be mentioned at the time he spoke has since developed into a real competitive problem to the cork stopper industry. This is the substitution of screw caps made of metal and molded composition for cork stoppers. This substitution and the resulting competition have developed not because of any superiority of performance by the screw caps; in fact, a screw cap will equal the stopper's closure performance only when bottle and cap are perfectly matched.

The production of cork stoppers by the American industry was first separately reported (values only) by the Census of Manufactures for 1923. The following table shows American production and imports for the years 1923-1940:

	AMERICAN PRODUCTION VALUE	IMPORTS VOLUME Pounds	VALUE Dollars
1923	$5,200,000	236,454	$275,564
1924		273,667	389,331
1925	6,739,000	367,792	380,839
1926		521,231	430,005
1927	6,294,000	385,754	583,803
1928		545,270	757,714
1929	7,195,000	290,336	209,437
1930		231,236	163,278
1931	3,382,000	88,354	58,376
1932		80,726	46,225
1933	2,826,000	236,759	167,821
1934		458,864	381,805
1935	3,429,000	186,371	152,613
1936		249,381	189,359
1937	3,680,000	276,142	212,203
1938		148,146	136,675
1939	3,184,000	269,002	191,411
1940	3,300,000 *	531,453	358,811

* Author's estimate; not a Government Census figure.

The shrinkage in the American production values shown in the above table is by no means all attributable to the competition from screw caps, but is the result of a number of factors, including screw-cap competition, reduced stopper prices and the depression which began in 1929. The repeal of prohibition in the United States is reflected in the data shown beginning with 1935.

THE COMPETITIVE PROBLEM—IMPORTED CORK STOPPERS

The cork stopper division of the industry is the one most subject to foreign competition. While a certain quantity of corks are still made by hand in foreign countries there are manufacturing plants in Spain and Portugal equipped with the same type of labor-saving machinery as used in the American plants, and these foreign manufacturers can and do export varying quantities of their production to this country as is shown by the table of imports opposite. While the total value of imported cork stoppers has seldom amounted to as much as ten per cent of the value of the total American production, the competitive impact of the foreign-made cork stoppers is much greater than a simple percentage comparison would indicate. This is due, in the first place, to the fact that the bulk of the imported cork stoppers is made up of a few common sizes and shapes principally of the wine bottle variety. These corks are the "staples" in the business, and it is on these that the importers of foreign-made corks concentrate rather than extending their competition over the whole line. In the second place, while the imports of foreign-made corks do not dominate the market in this country from a volume standpoint, they are nevertheless of sufficient volume to have a decidedly controlling effect on the price structure. In other words, it is the price at which the importer can afford to sell the foreign-made corks that establishes the price levels for all cork stoppers—both American and foreign-made—

of the type and sizes imported. This is the other "half" of the competitive problem in the American cork stopper industry, the first aspect being the competition from the other forms of closures discussed above.

Clutch corks—"first cousins" to bottle stoppers in appearance only. The specially-built machine shown inserts 108 corks in 55 seconds in the clutch plates used in a modern automobile. Cork is used in these clutch plates because of its high frictional quality discussed on pages 7-8.

[43]

The marketing of cork stoppers is relatively simple. Practically the entire American production is sold in this country; only insignificant quantities are exported, and, as mentioned in Chapter III, relatively few stoppers are sold by the manufacturers directly to the ultimate users. The customary unit of sale and pricing is a thousand stoppers and the manufacturers sell bulk shipments varying from a few thousand to a million or more on a single order. These sales are to five principal types of buyers, which are listed in the following summary in the order of their relative importance as customers of the industry:

1. Manufacturers of bottled products.
2. Dealers and wholesalers such as wholesale druggists, wholesale hardware and grocery establishments, dealers in brewers' supplies and scientific supply houses.
3. Manufacturers of bottles and closures.
4. Retailers of sundries such as chain stores and mail order houses.
5. Government departments and bureaus and educational institutions.

One thing more in connection with marketing and this is probably the most striking aspect of the business to an outsider. Partly because the sales of stoppers is almost entirely to various classes of dealers and partly for historical reasons going well back into the last century, the stopper manufacturers sell from price lists which are subject to very long trade discounts. At present (1938) for example, the price quoted by one manufacturer for a particular cork is $80.00 per M. That is 8 cents per cork, list price, but this list price is subject to a trade discount of 75%. And so on throughout the whole trade so that a stopper priced at several cents each on the manufacturer's price list may end up on the retail counter of the 5-and-10-cent store at 3 (or more) for 5 cents.

NATURAL CORK DISCS, DAUBERS AND SWABS

In addition to cork stoppers there are two other forms of natural cork closures, one of which is really a stopper with various attachments or additions. This latter is the dauber or swab or, as it is sometimes called, a cork applicator. An assortment of various types of these is shown in the photograph opposite, and it will be readily seen that they are basically a cork stopper with a wooden or composition top and a wire at the end of which there is a small tuft or pad to apply shoe polish or other liquid with which they are furnished. These daubers or applicators are made almost entirely on very ingenious automatic machines. The cork stopper is of course made in the usual way. Separate hoppers on the machines are filled, one with stoppers and the other with the tops; the wire is on a large spool and the padding or tuft material in large rolls. The machines automatically combine the separate parts into finished daubers at the rate of 75 or more per minute, notwithstanding the fact that at least twelve separate operations must be made.

These swabs or applicators are sold by the industry to manufacturers of liquid shoe polishes and cleaners and of various other liquids which can be applied with a dauber. The type made with a small glass rod instead of a wire and a tuft is used to apply various medicinal products locally to a cut, wound or callus. The manufacture of these daubers or applicators is a sub-division of the cork stopper industry and is not at all extensive. The entire American demand is supplied by four manufacturers, two of whom are also important stopper manufacturers.

The other form of natural cork closure is the cork disc used to

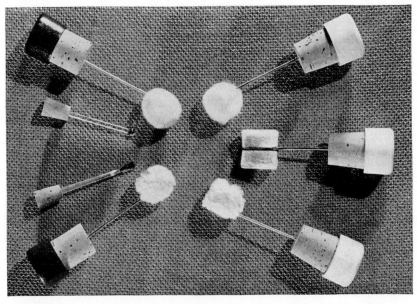

An assortment of daubers and swabs, each with a natural cork stopper.

some extent as a liner in screw caps and in some of the crowns used on carbonated beverage bottles. Here again it is the natural cellular construction of cork which makes a cork disc a very satisfactory cap or crown liner. When a crown or a screw cap equipped with a natural cork liner is fastened to the top of the bottle, the pressure exerted by the crimping of the crown or the screwing on of the cap compresses the cork down around the lip of the bottle and makes a very effective seal. Natural cork liners are not used as extensively as they once were due to having been replaced by the composition cork liner which will be discussed in a later industry chapter, but when crowns first came into widespread use natural cork liners were almost invariably used in them.

Natural cork liners are made by slicing thin sheets of cork wood on a plane parallel to the "back" or "belly" of the wood; that is, the sheets are sliced off the large flat surface of the bark and vary in thickness usually from $\frac{1}{16}$ inch to $\frac{1}{8}$ inch. The discs are simply punched out of these thin sheets.

It will be evident from the description of the manufacturing processes in the making of cork stoppers and cork discs and from the photographs in the preceding discussion that there is an enormous accumulation of cork waste in every cork stopper plant. This waste is a very valuable by-product of the manufacture of cork stoppers, inasmuch as the best cork wood grown is used for stoppers. A cork stopper plant therefore actually manufactures two products—stoppers or discs and cork waste. The latter is in two forms—blocker waste, being the strips or slices of cork wood from which stoppers or discs have been fashioned, and shavings from the tapering machines. None of this waste is wasted. It is sold to other industries and to the manufacturers of other cork products —insulation, composition and cork tile—but before concluding this discussion of the cork stopper industry we need to refer to the limited but nevertheless important production of various natural cork specialties.

NATURAL CORK SPECIALTY PRODUCTS

Natural cork specialty products are made in such a great variety of forms and shapes and for such a multitude of purposes that a complete listing and description of them is impossible here. They will therefore be covered very briefly in groups based primarily upon usage. This brief description, together with the accompany-

Natural cork specialty products. Balls, handle and penholder grips, fishing line bobbers, shuttlecock corks and gaskets—all made from natural cork.

ing photograph will serve to indicate the character and variety of these natural cork products. From a manufacturing standpoint all of them are quite simple. The natural wood is first cut into blocks of the proper size, squared and dressed, and the separate products are then either sawed out of these blocks, cut from them on large circular-knife machines, or turned on machines similar to ordinary woodworking lathes.

Floats and buoys. These, the oldest cork products, are still used extensively by fishermen and boatmen. Two thousand years after the ancient Romans first used pieces of cork as floats and buoys, science has yet to develop a material more buoyant and more durable under all kinds of marine conditions than is natural cork. (The manufacture of certain marine goods, notably life preservers and ring buoys, is a small but separate industry in itself and will be covered later.)

Natural cork specialties for industry. One group of these natural cork products is simply blocks or wheels of nicely finished natural cork. The blocks are used extensively by plasterers and while they have nothing to do with marine service, singularly enough, they are called floats. They are used by the plasterer to put a fine smooth finish on his work. The wheels are used largely for various kinds of polishing where a soft, velvety polishing surface is required such as in the polishing of plate glass, mirrors and chinaware. In addition to blocks and wheels natural cork is also cut in a great variety of shapes and sizes for use in industry as tank and carburetor floats, discs, washers and gaskets.

Sporting goods. Natural cork for various sport and game uses is made in the form of balls, handles, bobbers for fishing lines and even in the form of the bodies of ducks to be used as decoys. The handles are used extensively on fishing and casting rods on which they provide an excellent gripping surface.

Cork paper. Thin sheets of natural cork, known in the trade as cork paper and only 0.0025" thick, are sliced from cork blocks and are used extensively on the tips of cigarettes.

Lame lifts. Blocks of high-grade natural cork, called lifts, are used to build up the soles of shoes for lame people and are used extensively for this purpose because of the light weight and durability of cork.

Miscellaneous natural cork products. These vary from the staple, standard cork penholder grip which has been in use for a great many years to articles of wearing apparel and style novelties, the latter including buttons for ladies' clothes and hat ornaments.

As is the case in the production of stoppers and discs, the manufacture of these natural cork specialties results in considerable quantities of cork waste as the bark in its natural state is trimmed and squared and as the products themselves are cut or turned out of the wood. But none of these scraps are wasted; in fact, in no other industry is the by-product waste more important from a value standpoint than it is in the natural cork industry and in no other industry is the utilization of the by-product waste more complete than it is in the cork industry. The by-product waste of the natural cork industry becomes part of the raw material of the insulation, composition and cork tile divisions of the industry. The next chapters of this book are devoted to these.

CHAPTER V

CORK INSULATION—MANUFACTURE AND USE

THE insulation division is the largest and the most important from the standpoint of volume and value of product of the various divisions of the cork industry. This division manufactures five all-cork products as follows:

1. Corkboard
2. Cork pipe covering
3. Granulated cork
4. Isolation corkboard
5. Acoustical corkboard

These five products are insulators of various kinds. The first three are heat (or cold) insulators and are generally recognized as the standard materials in the low-temperature insulating field. As generally used, the function of cork insulation is to keep *out* heat or, conversely, to keep *in* cold. Cork insulation, in other words, does the reverse job of the heat insulating industry and products built on asbestos and magnesia. The fourth product listed above is a vibration (and noise) insulator, while the fifth acts as an insulator against the transfer of sound waves by a sort of "absorbing" process.

The earlier references in Chapters I and III to cork as an insulating material have indicated the *raison d'être* of the cork insulating industry. Once again, it is the cellular character of cork. At ordinary room temperatures and at low temperatures, next to a vacuum, a "dead-air" space minutely divided is one of the most effective heat (or cold) insulators known to modern science, and the bark of the cork oak, made up completely of tiny air-filled cells, is exactly such a "dead-air" space minutely divided. The job of a heat (or cold) insulator is the maintenance of an unbalanced condition against the unremitting efforts of natural forces to restore the balance. Whenever the temperature of a box, a room or a building is lowered (or raised) as compared with the surrounding temperature, Nature immediately sets in to bring about

Interior view of an ice cream hardening room showing how it is insulated with cork-board. The ceiling is also insulated with cork-board laid on top of the metal deck.

an equilibrium and it is the function of the insulating material to act as a barrier to prevent Nature from restoring the balance or equilibrium. The insulating barrier will do its work well or do it poorly depending upon the degree to which it will *not* conduct heat through the walls, ceiling and floor of the box, the room or the building.[1] Cork, in the form of boards, pipe covering and in loose granular form, is today the most generally used insulating barrier for the maintenance of low temperatures because it has a very low thermal conductivity; that is, it is one of the most effective nonconductors of heat available today.

1. CORKBOARD

Modern cork insulation was discovered quite accidentally, as mentioned in Chapter III, by one John T. Smith, a boat builder and ship chandler in New York City. Thomas gives the following interesting account of Smith's discovery:

"In the 'Boat Works' of John T. Smith on lower South Street . . . in New York, was a large cast-iron kettle with a fire box under it, the kettle being used to steam oak framing for row boats that Smith manufactured there for many years. He also produced boat fenders, life preservers and ring buoys, in the manner common in those days, by packing granulated cork in canvas jackets. Girls packed the cork in these jackets, using tin

[1] A further discussion of heat transfer and of insulation of particular interest to students of physics and engineering will be found in Appendix B, pp. 128-132. For a much more complete and detailed discussion, with special reference to cork insulation, see Pearl Edwin Thomas, *Cork Insulation.*

forms or cylinders to keep the canvas distended until filled. One of these cylinders became clogged in the hands of one of Smith's employees and was laid aside for the moment, but it inadvertently rolled into the dying embers of the fire box during clean-up late that evening.

Early the next morning, Smith, owner and fireman, cleaned out the fire box and found his misplaced utensil. But the hot ashes had not consumed the cork particles that had clogged it. The heat had been sufficient merely to bind the mass together in the form of a very substantial chocolate-brown cork cylinder.

Smith noted this peculiar fact with much interest, if not with actual astonishment, and put the tin form and cork cylinder aside for future secret study and investigation. He repeated the original and wholly unintentional experiment enough times to satisfy himself that for some good reason a certain degree of heat applied for a given time served to glue cork particles together without the addition of a foreign substance or binder of any kind or character, to produce what he later termed 'Smith's Consolidated Cork.' He thereupon applied for and was granted basic patents in the United States, Germany, France and England covering the broad principles involved."

Smith was granted United States Letters Patent No. 484345 on October 11, 1892. This patent rests on the following two basic claims quoted from the Letters:

"1. The process of treating cork, which consists in vaporizing the resinous matter contained therein by heating the cork in a mold or other suitable vessel under pressure, substantially as described.

2. The process of treating cork, which consists in moistening the cork, confining it in a mold or suitable vessel, and subjecting it to heat and pressure, substantially as described."

Grinding cork—4,800 bales, about 7,500,000 pounds—sufficient to make almost 5,000,000 board feet of corkboard.   [51]

Smith himself did not go into the manufacture of cork insulation, but in 1893 sold his patent to two other Americans, Messrs. Junius H. Stone and Harvey H. Duryee, who started manufacturing in Brooklyn, New York, later moving their company, first known as Stone & Duryee, then The Nonpareil Cork Works, and finally The Nonpareil Cork Manufacturing Company, to Camden, New Jersey. Messrs. Stone and Duryee first regarded the Smith patent as the basis for the manufacture of an asbestos-lined cork insulation for steam pipes and similar hot surfaces, but their progress with this material could not survive the competition which began in the 90's with the expiration of certain patents on "85% Magnesia" insulation for steam lines. It was at this point, according to Thomas, that the United States Navy became interested in the possibilities of cork insulation as a covering for cold pipes and brine lines to replace the hair felt formerly used and which was not particularly efficient because of its tendency to absorb moisture. These early experiments with cork covering on cold lines were successful from the start and its use spread to other branches of the Government.

"Thus the real field of usefulness for Smith's Consolidated Cork—as an insulating material for cold surfaces—was discovered; and soon thereafter, with the encouragement of the Navy Department again, the firm of Stone & Duryee began the manufacture of the very first pure corkboard that was ever produced, sold or used." [1]

THE MANUFACTURE OF CORKBOARD

For some years prior to this first manufacture of pure corkboard, there had been a small production in this country of the German-invented impregnated corkboard mentioned in Chapter III. Impregnated corkboard was soon found to be inferior to American corkboard made under Smith's patent and beginning about 1904, pure corkboard became the basic product of the industry.

As is the case with almost all cork products, the manufacturing of cork insulation is not an especially involved process. The raw material is the less valuable cork wood stripped from the trees and the cork waste from the stopper and natural specialty fac-

[1] Pearl Edwin Thomas, *Cork Insulation*, p. 31. Junius Stone continued to be actively identified with the cork insulation industry until his death in 1937; he furnished the author with some of the details of the early development of the industry given above.

tories. The cork wood used is largely "virgin" and "refugo"; the former is the bark of the first stripping of the tree, while refugo is the low-grade bark from the subsequent strippings. The waste is largely the blocker waste from the stopper factories, and both wood and waste are ground in enormous grinders with jaws large enough to take a whole bale at a time. From the grinders an air blower system transports the ground-up cork to the screeners in which the cork is cleaned of dust and screened into bins. It then goes to the presses where it is poured and compressed into metal molds or forms slightly larger in inside dimensions than the finished board in order to allow for trimming. The loaded molds then go into large ovens or are attached to super-heated steam lines

CORKBOARD INSULATION

Upper photograph: First step in manufacture; a bale of virgin cork at the mouth of the grinder.

Lower photograph: Finished corkboard in four different widths.

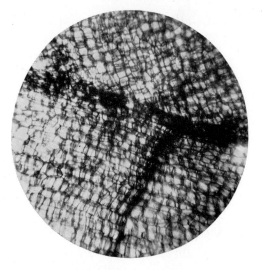

CORKBOARD UNDER THE MICROSCOPE

Microphotograph of a cross section of a piece of corkboard showing the joints between three granules of cork. Magnification = 100 x.

in order to bake the cork granules into solid blocks. In the oven process, the cork is baked from four to six hours, depending upon thickness, at a temperature of from 500° to 600° F., while in the steam-baking process the time cycle is considerably shorter at a temperature of approximately 600° F. No binding or other materials are added in the baking process; none are needed. Under heat and pressure, the natural resins in the cork bind the granules together in a homogeneous mass as shown in the accompanying microphotograph.

After the baking the blocks of corkboard are removed from the molds and allowed to cool. They then go to the trimming and splitting machines which trim the edges and split the blocks into various thicknesses varying from 1″ to 6″, the blocks as they come from the molds being of various thicknesses up to 15″. The stand-

Construction photograph showing how corkboard is erected in a cold storage warehouse.

ard area dimensions are 12″ x 36″ although some manufacturers make corkboard up to 36″ square. The finished product is very light and weighs only from about 6.5 to 9 pounds per cubic foot. After being trimmed and split it is packed in cartons and is ready for shipment.

THE USES OF INSULATION CORKBOARD

Considerable quantities of corkboard are used for insulating various kinds of refrigerating equipment including refrigerator cars, automobile truck bodies, the large refrigerators used by butchers and florists, and the ice cream cabinets and food display cases used in retail stores. The bulk of the product, however, is used for insulating rooms and whole buildings in the cold storage field, ice cream hardening rooms, fur storage vaults and for the insulating of roofs in textile and paper manufacturing plants and other industrial buildings in which the humidity in the atmosphere is very high. In all such plants, at certain temperatures, moisture tends to condense on the ceilings and, if permitted to do so, drips down on the men, products and machines in the plants. By applying a layer of corkboard to the roof deck of all such buildings the temperature of the ceiling surface can be kept at almost the temperature of the room itself, thereby minimizing or entirely preventing condensation and dripping. With the coming of air-conditioning,

Installing corkboard insulation
on the roof of the Adler Planetarium in Chicago.

[55]

increasing quantities of corkboard insulation are being used on the walls and ceilings of air-conditioned rooms and also on the cold air ducts and lines which carry the chilled air from the conditioning equipment to the rooms. Large quantities of corkboard insulation for this latter purpose are cut up into thin strips, called lagging, so that they can be used on the curved surfaces of pipes, ducts and tanks.[1]

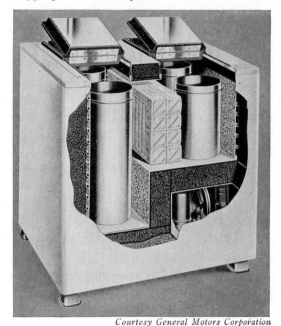

Courtesy General Motors Corporation

A modern ice cream cabinet insulated with four inches of corkboard as shown.

For all of these purposes corkboard insulation is today the generally accepted standard material, first, because of its superior insulating efficiency and, second, because of its high resistance to moisture penetration. Because water is an excellent conductor of heat, moisture is the big problem and the great evil in the low-temperature insulating field. Whenever the temperature of any surface drops below what is known as the dewpoint, which varies with the temperature and moisture content of the air, condensation occurs on the surface. Whenever a wall or a ceiling "sweats" this is what has happened, and there is a pronounced natural tendency for this condensation moisture to be driven or carried through the walls and ceilings. If this occurs and the moisture gets into the

[1] Prior to about 1930 large quantities of corkboard insulation were used to insulate domestic refrigerators, particularly of the newer electrical and mechanical type. However, as the competition among the manufacturers of these refrigerators became increasingly keen, and this in the midst of an economic depression, and also as improvements in the construction of the refrigerators permitted the use of insulating materials less efficient than corkboard, the latter was replaced by various cheaper substitute materials so that at present very few household refrigerators are lined with corkboard insulation.

insulating barrier, the effectiveness of the latter is greatly reduced and in time the barrier is likely to be completely ruined, particularly in those cases where the temperature is low enough to freeze the moisture that has penetrated the walls and ceilings.

Construction photograph showing corkboard insulation being applied to the ducts of the air conditioning system in the Capitol at Washington.

Because of the natural high resistance of cork to the penetration of moisture and liquids, corkboard insulation is highly resistant to the condensation moisture which is an ever-present menace in the low-temperature field. Unless the insulating barrier is protected, however, in time the natural forces at work would drive the moisture into even the best corkboard. The installation of corkboard insulation, therefore, is fully as important as its manufacture and this installation is a specialized trade in itself, done by the manufacturers and experienced contractors. In a good installation the corkboard is never put up "bare." Its natural resistance to moisture penetration is increased and supplemented by surface waterproofing, and, if more than one layer of corkboard is used, by a film of asphalt between the corkboard layers. This problem of proper installation is one on which the corkboard manufacturers have had to do even more research and experimenting than on the manufacture of the product itself. There are corkboard installations in the low-temperature field still giving efficient service which were erected twenty-five and thirty years ago and with the improved technique of today, a modern, properly-erected installation will probably last even longer. Most of the installations use either two or three layers of corkboard 2″ thick, making a barrier either

4″ or 6″ thick, but the thickness on many jobs is greater and in some cases will be as much as 10″ or 12″. The record job is one for an experimental room in which the cork walls are 18″ thick.

2. CORK PIPE COVERING

Cork pipe covering is made of the same materials as is corkboard and in the same manner up to the point of pouring into the molds. For the production of pipe covering the manufacturers have a large investment in metal molds by the use of which they make cork covering for pipe of various sizes and for every type of fitting encountered on a cold line such as valves, elbows, tees, crosses and all the rest. For very large pipes and cylindrical tanks the cork lagging referred to earlier in this chapter is used. Cork pipe covering is made in three thicknesses as follows:

1. Ice water thickness, 1.20″ to 1.93″ thick, for use on refrigerated drinking water and other cold lines in which temperatures of 35° F. and upward are carried.

2. Brine thickness, 1.70″ to 3.00″ thick, for brine, ammonia, carbon dioxide and low-temperature gas or liquid lines carrying refrigerants from 0° F. to 35° F.

3. Special thick brine, from 2.50″ to 4.00″ thick, for use on cold lines carrying refrigerants from −25° F. to 0° F. through areas in which the surrounding temperatures are high.

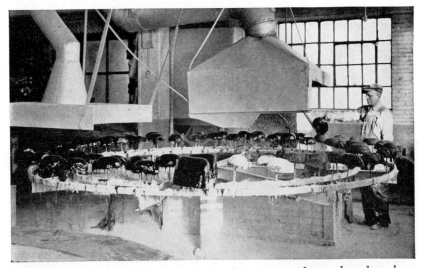

Making cork pipe covering. The cork pipe-fitting covers shown above have been molded and baked and each is being given a coating of hot asphalt.

An unprotected cold or refrigerant line is so obviously a waster of money that the need of insulating such lines adequately is generally recognized. But only those who have actually investigated the waste of refrigeration and

Cork pipe covering and fitting covers.

money which can be charged to an unprotected cold line know the real amount of this loss. A single uninsulated line of $1\frac{1}{2}$ inch pipe 200 feet long carrying brine at 15° F. through an area with a temperature of 90° F. wastes approximately $1\frac{1}{4}$ tons of refrigeration every twenty-four hours. This is a loss of over 450 tons of refrigeration in a year which, at an average cost of, say, $1.75 per ton means that this single uninsulated line is wasting almost $800.00 a year. The cost of insulating such a line with cork pipe covering would be made up several times during the first year's operation.

Cork pipe covering in service in a large ice cream manufacturing plant.

Cork pipe covering on the cold lines of refrigerating equipment.

Like corkboard, the natural resistance which cork pipe covering has to moisture penetration is supplemented and increased by a coating of asphalt on the inner and outer surfaces of the covering and all fittings. The molding of cork pipe covering is done so accurately that the finished material fits the pipes and fittings for which they were made with only a minimum of installation labor at the job. The covering and fittings are all furnished split in half and the pipes and fittings are encased in the covering by the use of wire and bands and the outside surface is then given a coating of black waterproof paint or the covered lines may be completely encased in a sewed canvas jacket painted to match the surroundings. The appearance of typical pipe covering installations is shown in the accompanying photographs.

3. GRANULATED CORK

Granulated cork, as the name implies, is simply ground-up cork and is used in low-temperature insulating work, usually in connection with corkboard. On many jobs there may be a space, for example, between two well-built walls, and by filling this space with granulated cork instead of lining the inner wall with corkboard an insulating barrier of adequate effectiveness can be provided.

Granulated cork is of two kinds—natural granulated and regranulated. The former is the by-product we mentioned in discussing screening in the manufacture of corkboard and is the finer granules which fall through the screens. In order to grade it into various sizes for various purposes it is given a grinding of its own and is designated in the trade by two numbers, such as $\frac{8}{14}$, $\frac{10}{20}$ and $\frac{20}{40}$, which refer to the mesh of the screens used in the grinding.

The second type of granulated cork, called regranulated, is ground-up trimmings and broken pieces of finished corkboard. Here again is a striking illustration of the complete lack of wastage which is an outstanding characteristic of the cork industry. All of the trimmings and any broken pieces resulting from the manufacture of corkboard go back to the grinders and are ground up just as is natural granulated cork and is then screened according to three trade specifications: (1) fine regranulated, (2) factory run or mixed regranulated and (3) coarse regranulated. Regranulated cork is a slightly better insulating material than is natural granulated cork, due to the fact that in the baking, various solids and excess resins were eliminated and the cells were all expanded slightly; regranulated cork therefore weighs less than granulated which means economies in handling and transportation.

4. ISOLATION CORKBOARD

Isolation corkboard is fundamentally very similar to insulation corkboard. The principal difference between the two is density, isolation corkboard being denser and therefore heavier than insulation corkboard. This greater density and weight are secured by packing more cork into the isolation board molds and compressing it under greater pressure. The standard size in isolation corkboard manufacture is 12″ x 36″; thickness varies from 1 inch to 6 inches but boards thicker than 4 inches are only infrequently used. This type of corkboard is made in various densities up to 24 pounds per cubic foot to carry loads varying from 400 pounds per square foot to 8,500 pounds and more per square foot.

The function of isolation corkboard is to reduce or eliminate the noise and destructive tendencies of the vibrations caused by machines in operation. Its use for these purposes results principally from two inherent characteristics of cork. One of these is again the air-filled cellular structure of cork and the second is its "reluctance" to take a set. As mentioned early in Chapter I, approximately 50% of the "solid" we call cork is really air—the air entrapped in the tiny cells. Therefore a machine standing on a

ISOLATION
CORKBOARD

Isolation corkboard in service.

piece of isolation corkboard is actually standing on a cushion 50% of which is air. This cushion absorbs most of the shocks and vibrations and the noise which would otherwise be transmitted to the floor, and this absorption results in greatly increased quiet and length of life of the machine.

Because of the fact that when cork is compressed what apparently happens is that most of the entrapped air within the cells is compressed, cork under pressure or weight struggles to recover its original volume, and in this struggle it never gives up completely. Isolation corkboard therefore retains its resiliency, so far as we know, almost indefinitely. One manufacturer reports that an isolation installation made in 1904 under a battery of heavy blowers is still giving satisfactory service. Like all vibration dampeners, isolation corkboard should be installed by trained engineers who must vary the density of the board in relation to the load and specify exactly how it is to be installed in order to make it do its job properly.

5. ACOUSTICAL CORKBOARD

From a manufacturing standpoint acoustical corkboard is also basically very similar to insulation corkboard. Its function is to absorb sound of all kinds from the most objectionable noise variety to the most pleasing concert music and voice of the singer. Through it the cork industry is identified with the increasingly important research program to control the unwanted and undesirable action of sound waves.

Sound is a form of energy created by something that is vibrating. This energy is transmitted in the form of waves which are spherical in shape and travel in all directions, becoming weaker the further they travel from their source. If completely unconfined, as they are in a large open country field, they very quickly dissipate and disappear into the atmosphere, but if they should strike a steep hillside at the edge of the field they may be reflected back as an echo. This echo out-of-doors is an interesting and often amusing thing, but in a confined area like a room or a hall this

Sound absorbing acoustical corkboard completely covers the ceiling of this high school gymnasium in Milwaukee.

[63]

reflection of sound waves, which is the echo out-of-doors, is a decidedly troublesome nuisance. It is to reduce or eliminate this nuisance that acoustical corkboard is used.

The acoustical corkboard ceiling of this classroom in a high school in James-town, N. Y., helps deaden the typewriter clatter.

In a room or a hall finished with rigid plaster walls approximately 97% of a sound wave striking such a wall is reflected back into the room, strikes the other walls, floor and ceiling, and continues back and forth until completely "used up." These reflections are known as reverberations; they add to the noise in the room and interfere with every subsequent wave. The problem therefore is to trap and hold these sound waves where they first strike the reflecting surfaces of the walls and ceiling of the room and this is what acoustical corkboard does.

The surface of a piece of acoustical corkboard is literally covered with sound wave traps. The slender cracks and the small spaces between the granulated particles which were not in actual contact during the baking make the surface of a sheet of acoustical corkboard full of circuitous interstices which break up the sound wave as it strikes the board and absorb it by a kind of trapping process in the cracks and spaces between the granules. This absorption is supplemented and increased by the fact that the exposed face of each cork granule presents to the sound wave an infinite series of little hollows which are the exposed cork cells, and which help trap the sound wave.

The importance of this problem of unwanted and excessive sound reflections has only recently been given the attention it has long deserved. For years the reverberations of sound have been particularly troublesome in institutions like hospitals where quiet is essential and in auditoriums and concert halls where practically perfect acoustics are necessary. There is now a scientific journal, the *Journal of the Acoustical Society of America,* devoted primarily to research in the source and control of sound waves and recent investigations in business offices, telephone exchanges, schools, stores and numerous other places where people congregate, have proved beyond question that excessive sound reverberations result in inefficiency, discomfort and economic loss. Acoustical corkboard is playing an increasingly important part in reducing these evils.

Acoustical corkboard is a light weight corkboard especially selected for surface texture and weighs only about 5.5 pounds per cubic foot. Its usual thickness is $1\frac{1}{2}$ inches and it is made in the form of tiles, sanded and beveled to improve their appearance. The sizes vary from 6″ x 1″ to 12″ x 36″. Being very similar to insulation corkboard, acoustical corkboard is a highly effective heat (or cold) insulating barrier and it therefore performs a double insulation function which is especially important when it is used in air-conditioned rooms, theatres and auditoriums.

Acoustical corkboard is erected usually by cementing or nailing it to an unfinished underwall of wood, plaster or metal. It can be and usually is painted for decorative effects, ease of cleaning and to increase light reflection.

A construction photograph showing the installation   [65]
of corkboard in the base of the skating rink of the St. Louis Arena.

CORK INSULATION—PRODUCTION AND IMPORTS

Partly because of the similarity of several of the products made by the insulation division of the cork industry it is impossible to show production statistics for each of the products separately. The Census of Manufactures for 1923 is the first Census report to show statistics of the insulation division separately. The Census for that year reported the value of cork insulation products manufactured but included the value of the cork tile production; this continued until 1935 when the tile data were given separately. The following tabulation showing the value of the cork insulation products manufactured by the American industry beginning with 1923 has been prepared from the Census data by eliminating from the figures for 1923 through 1933 inclusive an estimate of the value of the cork tile production included in the Census figures. This table, therefore, shows the combined production values of the five products discussed in this chapter.

CORK INSULATION DIVISION [1]
Value of Product—1923-1940

1923	$5,140,000
1925	5,830,000
1927	5,575,000
1929	9,100,000
1931	5,770,000
1933	4,860,000
1935	4,690,000
1937	8,580,000
1939	6,100,000
1940	7,500,000 *

* Author's estimate; not a Government Census figure.

For a number of years prior to 1932, imports of foreign-made cork insulation products entered this country in considerable volume, reaching a peak of almost 69,500,000 pounds in 1929. Beginning with 1932, imports declined steadily and drastically as compared with previous years. The reasons for this reversal are important aspects of the recent history of the industry. In the

[1] The adjustments made in the Census values as shown in this table for the years 1923-1933 inclusive have been made on the basis of information published in connection with the tariff revision of 1929-1930 and also on the basis of industry data available to the author. The figures beginning with 1935 include the Government values for corkboard and pipe covering plus the author's estimate for insulation granulated cork.

first place, the bulk of the imports of cork insulation products which came into this country during the years prior to 1932 was brought in by the American manufacturers themselves to supplement their domestic production which was insufficient to meet the country's requirements. Secondly, the increased duty on cork insulation products in the tariff act of 1930 resulted in the addition of two new American manufacturers to the industry in this country. Prior to 1931, one of these new manufacturers had been a large importer, while a distributor of the other new manufacturer had been one of the largest importers of cork insulation products in the country. Upon becoming an American producer, the first manufacturer stopped importing and so did the second manufacturer's distributor, thereby causing a considerable decrease in the volume of imports. At the same time the greatly decreased demand for cork insulation which set in in 1930 resulted in the other American manufacturers being able to meet the calls on them entirely from their domestic production. They therefore also stopped importing foreign-made cork insulation products and these facts account for the import shrinkage for the years 1932-1936.[1]

CORK INSULATION—MARKETING

The products of the cork insulation division are sold principally to two groups of buyers—(1) other manufacturers, (2) contractors. The first group includes the manufacturers of refrigerator cars and automobile truck bodies, manufacturers of refrigerators, food cabinets and florist boxes, the large meat-packing companies, and various other manufacturers who buy cork insulation products and install them in their own plants.

The contractors are the builders of cold storage plants and warehouses, breweries, ice cream manufacturing plants, textile mills, oil refineries, and all other buildings in which low-temperature areas are to be insulated.

The cork industry in general, and the insulation manufacturers in particular, believe it to be economically fair and wise to recognize the groups which make up the trade to which they sell on the basis of the functions performed by each group in the selling field.

---

[1] During 1937, imports of corkboard amounted to 2,854,090 board feet—the largest volume since 1931. Again, most of these imports were brought in by an American manufacturer to supplement his domestic production.

Broadly speaking, therefore, the insulation manufacturers recognize three different classes of buyers as follows:

1. Distributors
2. Resale and industrial buyers
3. Other buyers

The prices charged these various groups of buyers vary slightly, working up from that to the distributor whose price is the lowest because he actively engages in the marketing of cork insulation, works up business, pushes its sale, advertises the product, and in general takes over the selling functions most of which would otherwise have to be done by the manufacturers. The prices to the resale buyers are slightly higher than the distributors' prices because the resale buyers do not perform the selling functions which the distributors take over. The prices to the other buyers will be slightly higher than those to the resale buyers because ordinarily the other buyers perform no selling functions at all.

The insulation manufacturers also price their products to each class of buyers on a quantity bracket basis, recognizing either two or three sizes of buyers in each group. For a number of years past all of the manufacturers have sold their cork insulation products on a zone-delivered-price basis, which operates exactly like the Government's parcel post system. The whole country is divided up into a number of zones, and the price quoted a buyer is the manufacturer's plant price plus a charge for freight to the zone in which the buyer is located.

So much for the cork insulation industry built on a product discovered by accident in 1892 by a New York City ship chandler. That same year saw the invention of another article of much more widespread use—the so-called bottle crown. To the invention of the bottle crown is due in no small measure the development of the composition cork industry discussed in the next chapter.

CHAPTER VI

COMPOSITION CORK AND ITS PRODUCTS

COMPOSITION cork is frequently called the most versatile form of cork. It is made by one of the three largest branches of the cork industry. Unlike cork insulation, composition cork was not an accidental discovery. It was a laboratory development after years of research and it is made today by only a limited number of companies, each of which has its own manufacturing formulae. Actually, composition cork is for the most part natural cork and is produced by binding together small cork granules by the use of an adhesive binder in a manner very similar to the way in which the cork cells are held together by the resins in natural cork. The principal difference, therefore, between natural cork and composition cork is that in the latter part of the binding agent is synthetic. Various binders are used, depending upon the use to which the composition cork is to be put, the most common being glue, gelatin and synthetic resins. A hygroscopic material such as glycerin is usually added to the binding material and cork, binder and glycerin combine to make a product sometimes called "artificial cork," and "artificial" it is in the literal meaning of the term—"produced or modified by human skill and labor."

In the chapter on the cork stopper industry we referred to the use of natural cork discs as liners in crowns and screw caps. The modern crown was invented in 1892, and within ten years began to be widely used as a closure on bottles of beer and numerous carbonated beverages. This increasing use of crowns resulted in a greatly increased demand for high-grade cork wood for the manufacture of liner discs. With only a limited quantity of such wood available each year, natural cork liner prices climbed steadily and the need for another crown liner material became increasingly urgent. Then, during the first decade of this century, the technique of manufacturing in the young but rapidly growing automobile industry underwent the complete change which converted it into the mass production industry it is today, and this conversion resulted in an insistent demand for a new, resilient washer and

Composition cork in block form.

gasket material. During the early years of the automotive industry and continuing down until about 1905-1906, it was the general practice to make many parts, particularly of the motor, of cast iron or aluminum and all such parts had to be machined to a very smooth finish where they joined with other parts in order to make a tight fit and prevent leakage of oil, gasoline and vapors. Even with the machining of the surfaces it was customary to use a paper gasket shellacked to both parts so as to make the fit as tight as possible. During the years 1906 to 1908, in order to lower manufacturing costs and to reduce the weight of the finished automobile, the manufacturers, particularly of the less expensive cars, began to substitute pressed steel parts for many of the parts which previously had been castings. A pressed part is stamped out of a sheet of steel or other metal on an enormous press and such parts seldom have a surface sufficiently thick to be machined. To use them, therefore, called for a nonabsorbent gasket material of adequate thickness and resiliency to make a tight seal between two such pressed parts when bolted together. Paper would not do the job satisfactorily; neither would rubber because of the way in which it breaks down in contact with petroleum products, and felt could not be used because of its tendency to absorb oil and grease.

COMPOSITION CORK IS DEVELOPED IN THE RESEARCH LABORATORY

Here, then, was the two-fold demand which led to the development of modern composition cork. The bottling industry wanted inexpensive resilient crown liners while the automobile industry wanted an inexpensive resilient gasket material. Unlike cork insulation and cork tile, composition cork is made with a binder and it was the compounding of a suitable and satisfactory binder which was one of the chief problems that had to be solved before composition cork could be made available commercially. In order to be used on beverage bottles, for example, the binder had to be pure and wholesome and for use on all liquids it had to be as nearly inert or neutral chemically as it was possible to make it. There was also the very important problem of expansion and contraction, such as the gaskets used in an automobile motor would encounter, and this meant the compounding of a binder which would give composition cork an extremely low coefficient of expansion with changes in temperature and humidity.

During the 1890's, an American cork company began the manufacture of "artificial" cork made by mixing ground cork with an albumen binder; this material was widely used in the form of the grips on bicycle handle bars during the period of the so-called "bicycle craze" in this country. At about the same time, that is during the 1890's, an artificial cork material called "Suberit" appeared in Germany. This was made of ground-up cork and a collodion type of binder. In 1903 an American company bought a license to manufacture "Suberit" in this country, but for various reasons, including especially high cost, the development and use of this product did not last. The next development was a product called "Suberac," made by an American manufacturer out of ground cork and a shellac binder. Both Suberit and Suberac were forerunners of modern composition cork which first appeared during the years 1907-1908.

Here was the material needed by the automobile industry in order to go ahead with its mass-production program. Here was the material needed by the crown liner manufacturers and here too was a material which was an improvement on natural cork

Composition cork in sheet form and in two different granule sizes.

for the insoles of millions of pairs of shoes. Several years elapsed, however, after modern composition cork was first produced before it was available commercially in sufficient quantity and in a quality that would assure satisfactory performance. By about 1912, however, its initial development was complete and composition cork was in commercial production to meet the needs of the automobile and the crown manufacturers and of all the other industries needing a highly resilient, nonabsorbent material.[1]

Blocks of composition cork before and after boiling in an alcoholic solution of nigrosine dye showing how little dye penetrated the surfaces.

The product was first made of relatively coarse granules and in one weight or density. Its development has been continued during the 30 years since 1912, and composition cork is made today in at least fifteen different kinds, varying one from the other in granule size, type of binder and density. New types or kinds are constantly being introduced to add to or take the place of the previously used standard grades.

Cork composition is a truly remarkable combination of a natural product and man's inventiveness. A block of composition

[1] As is often the case with a product that has the experimental background that composition cork has, it is impossible to be more specific on dates than appears above. The product "evolves" in the laboratory; little in the form of historical records is kept and the experimenting manufacturer has every reason from a business standpoint not to publish reports on the progress made. Usually, therefore, the story has to be put together long afterwards and largely from the recollections of the men who developed the product. In the case of composition cork several of these men are still active in the industry and from them and the meager records available came the data for the summary above. In the 8 years, 1890-1897, there were three complete revisions of the tariff, one in 1890, another in 1894 and the third in 1897; the last of these is the first to mention composition cork (calling it "artificial or cork substitute"), which helps further to date the beginning of this product.

cork is only slightly heavier than a block of natural cork of the same size, and the composition block retains practically all of the inherent characteristics of the natural block. The photograph on the opposite page showing a composition cork block before and after boiling in nigrosine dye shows how resistant to moisture penetration this material is. Like natural cork, a block of composition cork has a very high degree of compressibility; it will not flow laterally to an appreciable extent while under pressure, and when the pressure is removed it quickly recovers its original thickness. These important characteristics of composition cork are shown in the photographs on this page. It has the same frictional quality as does natural cork because each surface of a piece of

COMPRESSION AND RECOVERY TEST ON A BLOCK OF COMPOSITION CORK.

Upper photograph: A block of composition cork 1" thick ready for the test.

Center photograph: The same block compressed to a thickness of ½" under a pressure of 240 pounds per square inch.

Lower photograph: The same block a few minutes after the release of the pressure showing recovery to practically its original 1" thickness.

composition cork presents a myriad of tiny fractured air cells which grip like vacuum suction cups; it retains this frictional power indefinitely and will not wear smooth or glaze with use and will not absorb oil or grease. While not especially designed to absorb vibration, as is isolation corkboard, composition cork, being essentially air-filled, cellular cork, is widely used in industry as a cushioning material. With certain binders it has much the same stability and chemical inertness as does natural cork and in addition to all these characteristics it does not have the limitations of size, thickness and grades of natural cork.

COMPOSITION CORK MANUFACTURE—RODS AND DISCS

The basic and primary products of the composition cork industry are the rod or cane and the block. As a rule, rods vary in length from a few inches to two or three feet, but by one process of manufacture, rods can be made indefinitely long. Blocks too are made in a great variety of sizes such as 24″ x 36″, 24″ x 48″, 29″ x 50″ and in thicknesses ranging from 1 inch to 6 inches. The first process in the making of both rods and blocks is the grinding and thorough cleaning of cork wood and cork waste which are then screened according to granule size. The size of the granule depends upon the purpose to which the finished product is to be put and is governed by the count of the screen mesh through which

Making cork composition rods for liner discs by the tube molding process.

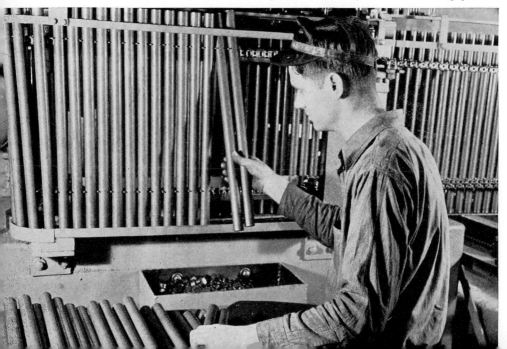

A battery of rod baking ovens.

the granules pass after being ground. These mesh counts vary from 30 to the inch, which produces a finely ground cork, to 5 or 6 to the inch, which produces a coarsely ground cork. After being screened the granules are thoroughly mixed in machines with the binder materials, and it is the exact formula for this mix which is the basis of production with every manufacturer of composition cork.

There are two different methods of manufacturing rods. By one method the mix is loaded into hoppers and is forced into hollow metal tubes by plungers. The inside diameter of the tube determines the diameter of the finished rod. The loaded tubes go into ovens in which the cork mix is baked for a period of from 20 to

In this battery of machines, almost a city block long, the composition cork rods are sliced into liner discs.

30 minutes at a temperature of from 200° F. to 250° F. The rods are then pushed out of the tubes and are stored for a seasoning period varying from several days to several weeks whereupon they are ready to be sliced on automatic machines into thin liner discs. This is the tube molding process.

The second method of rod manufacture is known as the extrusion process. Below the hopper in an extrusion process machine there is a battery of metal tubes each of which has a heating or baking element completely surrounding a short section of the tube. A small increment of composition mix is fed into each tube at regular intervals, packed and slowly pushed along the tube by a reciprocating plunger. The mix is forced through the tube at from 1 inch to 2 inches per minute and as it goes through the hot zone of the tube it is baked at a temperature of from 250° F. to 300° F. and is extruded at the end of the tube in the form of a rod which is cut off periodically by the workmen attending the machine. Some manufacturers using the extrusion process give the rods a second supplementary baking in ovens.

Instead of a solid rod, composition cork is also made by the extrusion process in the form of hollow cork tubes and in various other shapes of uniform cross section. These tubes and shapes are primary materials for various composition cork products of which the cork cot, used by textile mills in the spinning of yarns and threads, is a typical illustration.

Cork cots in service in a modern textile mill.

COMPOSITION CORK MANUFACTURE—BLOCKS AND SHEETS

In those manufacturing plants in which the block is the basic form the cork is ground and mixed with its binder in the same manner as in rod production, and after being thoroughly compounded, the mix is poured into metal molds, the dimensions of which determine the size of the finished blocks. These molds have adjustable and removable top and bottom plates, by means of which the mix is pressed into the molds and also by means of which the finished blocks are easily removed. The degree of pressure exerted on the mix in the mold determines the density and hardness of the finished composition. The loaded

A group of composition cork gaskets that helped make transportation history. The complete assortment of gaskets used in the Model T Ford.

molds go into the baking ovens, in which the temperature ranges from 200° F. to 250° F., for a period of from 8 to 10 hours or even longer. After cooling, the blocks are removed from the molds and stored for a seasoning period, as are the rods.

The second process with the block manufacturer is slicing or splitting. After being seasoned the blocks are sliced into thin sheets on machines similar to leather-splitting machines. These splitting machines look like band saws turned on their sides and with a band knife instead of a band saw. The sheets vary in thickness from ⅟₆₄″, which is about the thickness of a heavy sheet of paper, to ¼″ or in special cases even thicker. For many purposes these sheets are themselves finished products. They are used in this form, for example, in paper making and printing as backing pads and covering for rollers. But for many other purposes the sheet is a semi-finished product; out of it is cut a whole multitude of composition cork products varying in size and shape from simple liner discs to large oil pan gaskets and for a variety of uses varying from handles for ping-pong bats to grinding and polishing wheels. This cutting process is quite simple, the accuracy of the cutting die being the all-important feature. These dies are made from thin, cutting steel imbedded in a wooden or metal back. They are locked in presses and punch out the finished composition cork product, the number punched out in one stroke depending upon the thickness of the sheets, the design of the piece and the hardness of the material.

COMPOSITION CORK PRODUCTS

A complete listing and description of all the products made of composition cork is beyond the limits of this chapter. Instead of

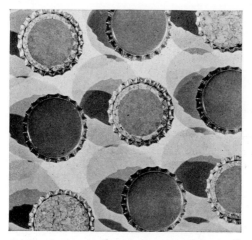

Bottle crowns each with a composition cork liner. Note the two spot crowns.

such a listing, therefore, the following summary of composition cork products, grouped according to principal use, indicates the range of the products made by this division of the industry.

Composition cork liners. These, a major product of the industry, in view of their widespread use and the earlier description in this chapter, need little additional discussion. They are used principally in the crowns on beer bottles and carbonated beverage bottles and as liners in metal and molded caps. Composition cork crown liners are used both plain and with facing materials, the latter type being known as spot crowns. A spot or disc of a protective coating made either of thin metal foil or coated paper, slightly smaller in diameter than the liner, is placed on the cork liner and is the only part of the crown seal which comes in contact with the bottled liquid. When a crown or screw cap with a cork liner is forced down on the lip of a bottle the natural compressibility and resilience of the cork makes a very tight seal, as

shown in the accom-
panying photographs
which also show the
sealing action of a
non-cork liner.[1]

*Gaskets, washers
and grease retainers.*
The general charac-
ter and use of these
products has also
been indicated in the
earlier discussion in
this chapter. The use

*Cut-away photographs showing the sealing action
of a composition cork disc compared with the
sealing action of a non-cork disc.*

of gaskets, washers and grease retainers is by no means confined
to the automotive industry. These products are made in an almost
endless variety of sizes, shapes and thicknesses. They serve as
the seal usually between two metal parts and almost invariably
wherever such a seal has to be effective against oil or grease or
other petroleum products. It has frequently been said that without lubricating oil and grease no engine or machine in the world

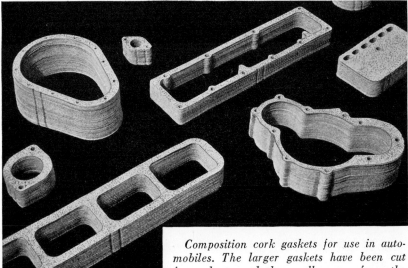

*Composition cork gaskets for use in auto-
mobiles. The larger gaskets have been cut
from sheets and the smaller ones from the
center areas cut out of the larger gaskets.*

[1] A much more complete description of cork as a liner material is included
in a booklet, "Cork—The Live Liner," published by the Cork Institute of
America.

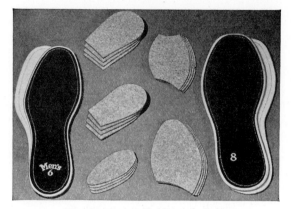

Composition cork shoe products.

could turn a wheel; it is equally true that many of these engines and machines in operation today would stop without a cork gasket, washer or retainer to keep the oil and grease at work.

Shoe products. Cork has been used in the making of footwear for at least 2,000 years. Prior to the development of composition cork, inner soles for shoes were made of thin sheets of natural cork and one of the earliest substitutions of composition cork for natural cork was as inner soles for shoes. Composition cork is now used at four different points in the making of a pair of shoes. In women's shoes made by the McKay process the insole is made of composition cork. In the better grade of men's shoes the box toe (in the toe of the shoe) and the counter (in the heel) are frequently made of composition cork. The fourth point is the so-called bottom filler used between the insole of the shoe and the outer sole. Composition cork is widely used as a

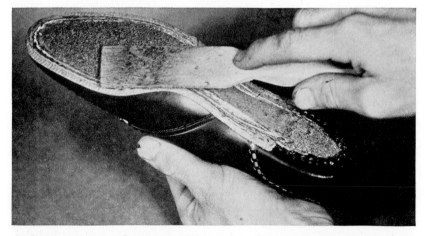

Cork composition used as bottom filler in shoes helps make them flexible, light in weight and moisture-resistant.

bottom filler and its use at one or more of these four points in a pair of shoes helps make the shoes flexible, damp-proof and at the same time aids in keeping them light in weight.

Industrial products. Enough has already been said in this chapter to indicate the almost endless variety of cork composition products made for use in industry. In the textile and the paper-making mills, composition cork is used in the form of cork cots

Cork polishing wheels. The wheel in the right foreground is made of natural cork. The others are made of composition cork.

described above and as a roller covering material. In the printing of our daily newspapers composition cork is used in the form of stereotype blankets, which are employed in the process of transferring the impression of the block of a negative type set by the linotype machine to a positive on a specially prepared paper board which is later used for making a negative on the metal casting which goes into the printing press.

In the glass and pottery industries grinding and polishing wheels are made of composition cork. In the machinery industry, composition cork in addition to its use as gaskets, washers and grease retainers, is used in the form of discs in friction clutches of various types. Throughout industry generally and in many of its products composition cork in various forms is used as a cushioning material and vibration dampener. This list can be expanded almost indefinitely as will be seen from the detailed list of products given in Appendix A.

Building and construction materials. In the building and construction field composition cork is used in the making of modern concrete roads and in the erection of various concrete structures, retaining walls and the like. In the building of a concrete road, for example, composition cork is used as an expansion joint material between the sections in which such a road has to be built in order to allow for the expansion and contraction caused by the heat of summer and the cold of winter. If this expansion and contraction were not allowed for the road would buckle and bulge in the summer and after a first severe winter it would be badly cracked. To avoid this and to compensate for the difference in the length of the road when hot as compared with its length when cold, the road is made in sections and a sheet of compressible material is put between the sections. This permits the road to expand in the summer, compressing the joint-filling material, and when the road contracts in the winter the material expands and keeps the space between the sections filled. Various materials besides composition cork are used for this purpose but composition cork has an advantage over most of them due to the fact that when heat causes the road to expand most of these other materials bulge out of the joint and come above the level of the road, thus making

The expansion joint material—composition cork—between the sections of this concrete road on Long Island will never bulge above the surface.

[82]

an annoying and destructive bump at every joint in the road. Composition cork expansion joint material on the other hand does not bulge above the road surface when it is compressed; it thereby makes for pleasanter driving and saves the incalculable wear and destruction to both

A group of composition cork novelty products.

cars and road caused by the steady pound, pound, pound of cars and trucks striking an expansion joint material which bulges at the section joints when compressed.

Composition cork is also used in buildings as a wall covering material for its beauty and decorative effect and as a bulletin board material because it makes such an excellent base for posting temporary notices and bulletins by means of thumb tacks. The cork holds the thumb tack with a very strong grip but readily permits it to be pulled out and then shows no hole where the tack was used. Composition cork for these purposes is made in long rolls on linoleum-making machines. Its production will therefore be referred to again in the chapter on linoleum.

Sporting goods. Composition cork is used on the handles of golf clubs, ping-pong bats and other similar articles and equipment. It is also frequently used on the striking surface of the ping-pong bat and as a surface material on various games and playing surfaces especially in those which use a dart of any kind. A small composition cork ball is the foundation on which high-grade baseballs are built.

Miscellaneous. Some cork stoppers are made of composition cork instead of natural cork, and in various novel shapes and forms composition cork is used for the making of buttons and ornaments on women's clothes, as coasters for use under glasses, as bath mats, as a counter and table-mat material, as a surface material for stools and chairs and as an integral part in numerous novelty and standard articles of everyday use. Cork paper for cigarette tips can now be made of composition cork. This is one of the most recent developments in the industry.

SIZE OF THE INDUSTRY

The available production statistics for the composition cork industry are very meager and unsatisfactory. The Government's Census of Manufactures for 1935 is the first to show separate values for the composition cork industry. In that year the industry's production, according to the Census, amounted to approximately $2,600,000, but this total, and also the 1937 value, quite evidently did not include the value of the composition cork liners produced by crown manufacturers who are not otherwise in the cork business. The following tabulation shows the value of the composition cork products manufactured as reported by the Government Census with adjustments for the years 1935 and 1937 for the reason given above:

COMPOSITION CORK AND PRODUCTS—VALUE OF MANUFACTURE
1935-1940

	1935	1937	1939	1940
Cork Gaskets, Discs, Wafers and Washers	$1,618,600	$2,060,000	$3,146,400	Author's
All Other Finished Products..	991,700	1,535,000	1,853,500	Estimate
Government Census Totals ..	$2,610,300	$3,595,000	$4,999,900	Details
Estimated Value of Crown Liners not included above	1,600,000	1,700,000	Included	not Available
TOTAL	$4,210,300	$5,295,000	$4,999,900	$5,500,000

For the alternate years from 1923 through 1933, the Census reports on the cork industry include the value of the composition cork products manufactured in a classification entitled "Value of cork specialties and products, not elsewhere specified." This classification apparently also includes the production values of cork marine goods, natural cork specialty products, and "all other" finished cork products. As in the case of the 1935 production discussed above, the value of the cork liners manufactured during those years by the non-cork companies is evidently not included in the Government figures. With such complications and omissions, it is impossible to break down the statistics for the years prior to 1935 in order to arrive at even an estimated value of the composition cork products manufactured during these earlier years. It is possible, therefore, to say here only that the value of the composition cork products manufactured by this division of the industry from 1923 through 1940 has ranged between approximately $3,000,000 and $6,000,000.

MARKETING COMPOSITION CORK PRODUCTS

Cork composition products are sold overwhelmingly to other manufacturers either in the form of blocks and sheets or as finished products such as liners, gaskets, washers, textile cots and shoe products. All of the manufacturers of composition cork liners also make completely finished crowns, and their liner sales therefore are either in the form of finished crowns or as liners both plain and faced. The finished crowns are sold to the breweries and to the bottlers of various food products and beverages. These crown sales are often in carload quantities, a standard carload being 30,000 gross. The liners themselves are sold principally to the cap manufacturers, whose customers are the distilleries, wineries, and the manufacturers of medicinal, extract, cosmetic and similar preparations.

In the form of sheets, gaskets, and washers, composition cork is sold to the automotive industry and trade and to other manufacturers of machinery and equipment. All of the manufacturers of blocks and sheets also cut finished gaskets. As a rule, it is more economical for an automobile, an engine, or a machinery manufacturer to buy his finished gaskets directly from the composition cork manufacturer because of the valuable side product which results from gasket cutting. When a large oil pan gasket, for example, is cut out of a sheet of composition cork the center area can be cut up into smaller gaskets, discs, and washers for which the cork manufacturer has a ready market. The usual pricing unit in the marketing of sheets, gaskets, and washers is 1,000 pieces; an order may call for 50,000 or more pieces or it may be for only a few units.

Cork shoe products are sold almost entirely to the manufacturers of shoes and generally priced in quantities of 1,000 pieces, while the whole group of industrial products is sold to a large and varied group of machinery and equipment manufacturers. Here again the usual pricing unit is 1,000 pieces.

Expansion joint material and bulletin board are sold to road builders and building contractors on a footage basis.

The sporting goods and miscellaneous products are also sold to a varied group of other manufacturers. In the case of these products, the selling quantity may be as small as a dozen pieces.

In other words, like the other divisions of the cork industry, the composition cork division is distinctly not a consumers' goods industry, and usually the ultimate buyer of composition cork does not even know he is buying it. In an automobile, for example, the composition cork is so inconspicuous as to be truly invisible to the car buyer; and yet so important is composition cork in the manufacture of automobiles that a break in the supply of some small, inexpensive composition cork part would mean at least a temporary stop in the assembly lines in most of the automobile plants in the country.

CHAPTER VII

CORK TILE[1]

CORK tile is a flooring material and is also now being used in increasing quantities as a wall-covering material. Its outstanding characteristic is its resiliency. Except only a carpet or a rug, it is the most resilient flooring material available today. Like insulation corkboard, cork tile is made entirely of natural cork and contains no binders or other foreign materials. Most of the cork tile made by the American industry is made primarily from the cork shavings which result from the tapering of natural cork stoppers described in Chapter IV, but since 1937 one American manufacturer has been producing European-type cork tile made from a specially-ground cork.

The manufacture of cork tile was begun in this country about the year 1900. Until 1920, the industry remained small and relatively unimportant; the combined production for that year of all the American manufacturers (four in number) amounted to only about 200,000 square feet. During the next ten years, however, with the development of the product completed, production expanded over fifteen fold and in 1927 amounted to just short of 3,000,000 square feet. With the great falling off of new building construction which followed the economic collapse of 1929, the market for cork tile was reduced to only a fraction of its pre-depression size, but as the building industry recovers, the cork tile industry should recover much of its lost market.

The manufacture of cork tile, except for the type of cork used, is fundamentally quite similar to the manufacture of insulation corkboard. After being cleaned and ground (the shavings are cut up into smaller pieces) the cork is packed into molds in large hydraulic presses. It is then baked in the molds for a period of

[1] The Federal Trade Commission has recently ruled that the word "tile" standing alone can only be used commercially to designate a ceramic product or a product made of baked clay, and that whenever the word tile is used to designate a non-ceramic product, the name of any such product must include a word or words indicating the material from which the product is made, as for example, cork tile.

[87]

from seven to ten hours at a temperature varying from 450° to 600° F. As in the case of the cork insulation products, this baking melts the natural resins in the cork and thereby binds the granules or the shavings into a solid homogeneous mass. The most interesting aspect of the baking process is that its duration and temperature control the color of the finished tile.

CORK TILE MANUFACTURE

After the mold has been loaded with cork shavings it goes into an enormous hydraulic press which compresses the loose shavings to the required density. The compression is maintained during the baking by steel rods inserted in the slots shown in the mold.

Cork tile is made in three shades of brown designated as light, medium and dark. The light shade is approximately the same color as a natural cork stopper, while the dark shade, at the other extreme, is a chocolate color. The color variations result entirely from the duration of the baking time and the temperature used; the longer the baking time or the higher the temperature, the darker the shade of the tile.

The duration and temperature of the baking also have a direct bearing on the weight of the tile although weight is primarily dependent upon the quantity and quality of the cork used. The lighter the color of the tile, the heavier it is; this is due to the fact that the longer the tile is baked or the higher the baking temperature, the more thoroughly the inherent moisture in the cork is driven out and the more thoroughly the resins are dried out. These weight differences which result from the baking are of course very slight, being only a few ounces per square foot.

A loaded cork tile mold starts on its 8-hour trip through the baking oven.

The standard thicknesses for cork tile are $\frac{5}{16}''$ and $\frac{1}{2}''$; both thicknesses are made in a variety of sizes in square and rectangular shapes, the standard sizes varying from $3'' \times 3''$ to $18'' \times 36''$. Cork tile is also made in the form of a cove base so that a cork tile floor can be extended up the wall of a room with a rounded joining between the floor and wall base. Until recently the product was made only with squared edges, but in 1935 the manufacturers began making tile with the edges of the wearing surfaces beveled.

Cork tile is installed by simply cementing it to the wall or floor surface. The square-edge tile is sanded after being laid, but the bevel-edge tile does not require this sanding operation, due to the fact that the beveled edges automatically take up or compensate for any minor irregularities in the sub-floor. The finished job may be varnished or waxed, or both varnished and waxed, all depending upon the wishes of the customer.

The wishes of the customer also determine the pattern of the finished floor. These pattern possibilities are many and varied and, singularly enough, there is quite a style vogue in them. Most patterns utilize two different shades of tile and about the most standard possible pattern is a checkerboard design of alternate light and darker brown squares usually combined with some form of border. Right now the tendency among architects and builders is to lay cork tile "at random." In such installations the natural variations in a color provide the contrast and usually a random installation will use tile in several different sizes.

As already mentioned, the outstanding quality of cork tile as a flooring material is its resilience. This resilience, which again is due entirely to the air-filled cellular structure of natural cork, makes a cork tile floor a very comfortable surface for those who walk or stand on it, and this same resilient characteristic also results in a cork tile floor being a very quiet floor. Particularly because of this latter feature, cork tile is extensively used as a flooring material in hospitals, schools, libraries, art galleries, banks, auditoriums, churches, court rooms and in various public buildings where footfalls are decidedly nuisance noises. It is also extensively used in business offices where it helps materially to reduce the noise and vibration caused by typewriters, accounting machines and similar office equipment. Because of its natural resilience, a cork tile floor is very long-lived; frequently, an installation after years of service is resanded and refinished and looks like a newly laid floor.

In addition to its characteristic of resiliency, a cork tile floor is highly nonabsorbent of any liquids which might be spilled on it, again because natural cork itself has a high resistance to liquid penetration. Finally, because of the low thermal conductivity of

[90]

Cork tile on the walls of a modern business office.

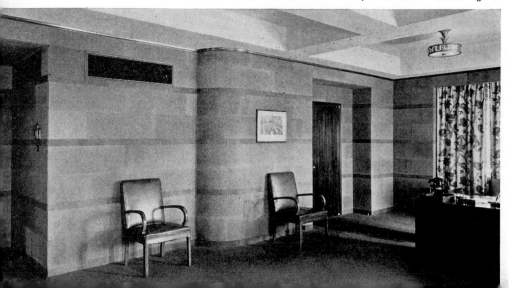

cork in any form, cork tile makes a warm floor in cold weather and a cool floor in hot weather.

The Census of Manufactures for 1935 is the first to show the value of the cork tile production separately—$109,000. Previous Census reports, going back to 1923, included the value of the cork tile manufactured with the value of the cork insulation products; this was referred to in the statistical summary in Chapter V where the production statistics for cork insulation products were adjusted by eliminating an estimated value for the cork tile production. Using these same adjustment figures for the years 1923 through 1933 and adding the data for subsequent years gives the following table for cork tile production from 1923 to date:

CORK TILE DIVISION [1]

Value of Product Manufactured—1923-1940

1923	$375,000
1925	450,000
1927	600,000
1929	505,000
1931	255,000
1933	120,000
1935	109,000
1937	253,000
1939	220,000
1940	210,000

[1] The adjustments made in the Census values as shown in this table for the years 1923-1933, inclusive, have been made on the basis of information published in connection with the tariff revision of 1929-1930, and also on the basis of industry data available to the author. The 1927 peak-year production was estimated as 2,983,500 square feet by an American manufacturer in his testimony in connection with the tariff revision of 1929-1930. The value for 1940 is the author's estimate.

A modern brokerage office floored with beveled cork tile.

The very substantial shrinkage in these figures for the last years shown is due primarily to the great decrease in new building construction which has been one of the most prominent features of the economic depression which began in the fall of 1929. The cork tile industry is so closely allied with the building industry that production varies with the ups and downs in the construction industry except that there will be a lag of from six months to a year or more between an increase or a decrease in new building construction and an increase or a decrease in the production of cork tile due to the fact that the flooring material is one of the very last of the installations in a new building.

CORK TILE IN THE
MODERN HOME

Left: Cork tile used as a wall covering.

Below: Cork floor tile in a modern living room.

Cork tile is marketed through flooring contractors, most of whom are local operators confining their activities to a particular city or area but a number of the larger ones cover an extended territory. Very few of these contractors carry a large stock of cork tile. Instead, a flooring contractor will submit an estimate for doing a particular cork tile job and if he is awarded the contract he then orders the necessary quantity of tile for the job from the manufacturer. Most of the business has to be done in this way because almost every cork tile installation is an individual custom-made job. The purchaser or his architect decides on the thickness of the tile to be used, on the design he wants, the sizes of tile, and whether they are to be square-edge or beveled. With so many variable factors it will be evident why the flooring contractor waits until he is awarded a contract before ordering the tile from the manufacturer.

Cork tile flooring laid at random in a college library.

Cork tile is priced and sold by the manufacturers on a square foot basis. Almost always the final purchaser buys the tile in the form of the finished floor—contracting with the contractor to install the tile for a given over-all price which includes all the material and installation labor.

In addition to its use as a floor- and wall-covering material, cork tile is also used in the manufacture of table tops, trays and checkerboards and chessboards. It is ideally suited for the latter; two shades—a light and a medium brown—provide the alternate colored squares required for these games and the resiliency of the cork makes for an ideal quiet playing surface.

Cork tile is not a cheap flooring material, being in a sort of middle price range between less expensive materials, like linoleum, and other more expensive forms of flooring. It is competitive with all these other materials, however, not so much from the standpoint of price as it is from the standpoint of its outstanding characteristic—resiliency.

CHAPTER VIII

CORK MARINE GOODS

So far as the cork in them is concerned cork marine goods might be classed with the natural cork specialty products. In fact, certain of the simpler cork products used in fishing and boating are considered in the industry as natural cork specialty products and were covered in Chapter IV on cork stoppers and natural cork specialties. These simpler products include seine and gill corks, floats and mooring buoys—all of them marine goods from the standpoint of use, and all of them made by the stopper and natural specialty division of the industry. What then, it will be asked, are the products of the marine goods division and why regard it as a separate division of the industry?

The products are three—cork life preservers, cork ring buoys and cork fenders and bumpers for yachts and small boats. The manufacturers of these products are generally considered a separate division by the industry itself, first, because of the close supervision which the Federal Government exercises over the two principal products of this division of the industry—life preservers and ring buoys. A manufacturer of these two products has to be approved by the Bureau of Marine Inspection and Navigation of the United States Department of Commerce, and every life preserver and 30-inch ring buoy he sells must bear the Government's stamp of approval.[1] In the second place, the marine goods division of the industry combines cork with other products, chiefly cotton duck, so that in its output cork is only a part although a most important part. In the third place, the trade to which this division of the industry sells its products includes a very different class of customers than the class that buys floats and buoys; the

---

[1] This supervision goes back to 1871. An earlier Act, the Steamboat Act of 1852, required that passenger vessels be provided with life preservers made of suitable material or floats well adapted to the purpose, but the Act of 1871 provided for the supervision and approval by Federal Government authorities of vessels' life-saving equipment. According to the files of the Bureau of Marine Inspection and Navigation, one T. B. Boyd of Chicago, on June 15, 1871, submitted the first life preserver for approval by the Federal authorities.

customers of the marine goods division are principally the large steamship and ferryboat companies, the railroads that operate water transportation systems and the dealers in ship supplies.

From the standpoint of product usage, the marine goods division can rightfully claim to be the oldest division of the cork industry. Because of its light weight and buoyancy cork was used as floats and buoys by the ancients and when a Roman soldier swam the Tiber some 2,000 years ago with the help of some pieces of cork he was using an improvised life preserver. As mentioned in Chapter I, the use of cork as a buoyant material was so well known to the ancient Romans that it accounted for a most interesting idiomatic expression in Latin. The phrase *"nare sine cortice"* means literally "to swim without [the use of] cork," but this same phrase was also used idiomati-

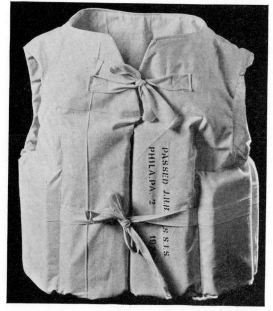

Cork life preserver—adults' size. Notice the Government's stamp of approval showing the inspector's initials.

cally to mean "to need no [more] assistance." The marine goods division of the cork industry may also lay claim to a full measure of credit for the establishment of the cork insulation industry, for, as indicated in Chapter V, it was a cork marine goods manufacturer who discovered the process of making cork insulation which is today the basis for this largest division of the cork industry.

The industry's major product is the cork life preserver, sometimes called a jacket and sometimes a belt. So far as the cork itself is concerned the manufacture of a life preserver is principally a cork cutting business using thick natural cork in relatively large pieces. The present Government regulations require that each adult-size cork life preserver shall contain a minimum of

Seine floats made from natural cork.

5½ pounds of cork. This cork is cut out of the natural wood in the form of blocks, which are then sewed into the pockets of the canvas or duck jacket, every detail of which down to the size and type of thread used must pass the Government's inspection. To pass the Government's inspection an adult's life preserver must support a dead weight of twenty pounds of iron in water. The average human being, when completely submerged, weighs approximately one-tenth as much in water as in air; therefore, a cork life preserver that will support twenty pounds dead weight of iron in water will support an average human being weighing approximately 200 pounds, dead weight, in the water.[1] Life preservers are also made in a size for children; these each require about three pounds of cork and must have a dead-weight buoyancy of ten pounds.

The second principal product of the marine goods division is the cork ring or life buoy illustrated on the next page. These rings are made in various sizes—15″, 17″, 19″, 20″, 21″, 25″, 27″ and 30″ outside diameter—but only the 30-inch ring buoy is recognized and approved as Government standard. With an outside diameter of 30 inches, this buoy has an inside diameter of 17 inches; the cork ring therefore is 6½ inches across and is oval in cross section, 3 inches through at the thickest point. These cork rings are made up of a number of pieces of cork very securely fastened together by the use of insoluble glue and wooden

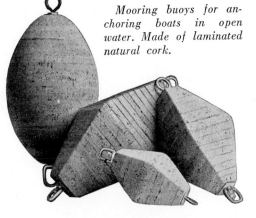

Mooring buoys for anchoring boats in open water. Made of laminated natural cork.

[1] Human bodies vary in their buoyancy. A muscular athlete, for example, is not as buoyant as most "fat" men. Hence the reference to "average" above.

dowel pins. As is the case with life preservers, every manufacturer of 30-inch ring buoys must be approved by the United States
Government and every such ring buoy he makes must meet the
Government specifications, all to the end of increasing the safety
of life at sea.[1]

In the case of both life preservers and ring buoys cork is used
as the buoyant material again because of its natural air-filled cell
structure. Because of this cellular structure cork has a specific
gravity of only ap-
proximately .25 and
a life preserver and
ring buoy made of it
will support a human
body in the water and,
equally important, it
will do so almost in-
definitely. This sec-
ond factor is the re-
sult of cork's natural
resistance to water
and liquid penetra-
tion. If a life pre-
server or a ring buoy
is to do its job at all
it must do it so long
as the wearer is in
the water and only
a nonabsorbent buoy-
ant material can be

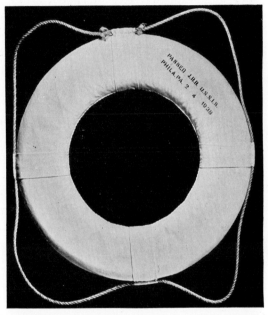

*30-inch cork ring buoy passed by an inspector of
the United States Steamboat Inspection Service.*

counted on from this standpoint. Cork is exactly such a material
and is used in the production of life preservers and ring buoys
because of its buoyancy and its highly nonabsorbent characteristic.

The third product of the marine goods division of the cork industry is relatively much less important than the life preserver
and the ring buoy. It is the cork bumper or fender for which an
old worn-out automobile tire is often substituted by many boatmen. The cork fender or bumper is simply a canvas sack in the

[1] Effective January 4, 1941, life preservers containing $4\frac{1}{2}$ pounds of cork
with a dead-weight buoyancy of $16\frac{1}{2}$ pounds and 24″ and 20″ ring buoys are
Government approved for use on motor boats not carrying passengers for hire.

shape of a tube filled with granulated cork. It serves as a cushion or bumper to protect small yachts and boats from damage from piers, bulkheads and piles when they are docking.

Cork has its competitors in the marine goods field—the principal ones at present being balsa wood and kapok. The former is a very light weight wood familiar to most people as the wood used in the making of toy and model airplanes. Kapok is a fibrous material obtained from within the seed pods of a tropical tree (*Ceiba pentandra*). Recently, too, an expanded rubber material has been developed but thus far this has not become an important factor in life preserver manufacture. Against all of these substitute materials cork has maintained its position and is the standard material in the manufacture of life preservers and ring buoys for use especially on larger boats and transoceanic steamships.

Figuratively, the industry goes from a feast to a famine. During the War years 1917 and 1918, when all kinds of shipping materials were urgently needed, whole carloads of life preservers were shipped by express in fast passenger trains. Today freight shipments are the rule.

Never a large industry in this country, the marine goods division of the cork industry varies in size with the fluctuations in

[98]

The S.S. "America" of the United States Lines arrives in New York harbor equipped with 1,850 adults' life preservers, 185 children's life preservers and 24 ring buoys.

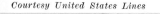

Courtesy United States Lines

American shipbuilding. It does not, of course, include in its market the large ocean-going vessels and liners which are built in foreign countries, all of which are fitted out with their life-saving equipment where they are built. Instead, its whole market is the shipbuilding industry in this country and the United States Navy. There is only a limited replacement or renewal business so far as the cork is concerned because the cork blocks and sections in a life preserver or a ring buoy last indefinitely. The canvas jacket part may need replacing and when it does, it is simply a case of recovering the cork blocks or sections.

The twenty-year "armistice" that ended in 1939 was a succession of lean years for the cork marine goods industry due largely, of course, to the limited volume of new shipbuilding in this country during that period. The Census of Manufactures for 1935 is again the first to report a separate value for cork marine goods produced in this country. The following summary shows these data from that year to the latest available.

LIFE PRESERVERS, LIFE-PRESERVER BLOCKS AND CORK FLOATS
Value of Manufacture—1935-1940

1935	$270,000
1937	384,500
1939	354,500
1940	300,000 *

* Author's estimate; not a Government Census figure.

The types of buyers who make up the market for cork marine goods have already been indicated in this chapter. They are the large shipbuilding companies and the builders of small boats and yachts, the railroads that operate ferryboat and water transportation systems, the United States Government and the dealers in marine goods and boat supplies. In this country, too, a great many municipal governments operate a ferryboat service and such city governments are substantial buyers of life preservers and ring buoys under the usual system of advertising for bids for a specified quantity of life preservers and ring buoys, the low bidder getting the order.

In the sale of life preservers most of the manufacturers use five quantity price brackets for orders which vary in size from those for less than a dozen life preservers to orders for a full carload. An average size freight car will hold approximately 2,500 life preservers and in times of good business and activity in the American shipbuilding industry, sales of life preservers in carload quantities are not at all infrequent.

In the sale of ring buoys, which are used in much smaller numbers than life preservers, three quantity brackets are recognized by most manufacturers in their price lists. The first and highest price is for less than 12 buoys, the intermediate price is for quantities from 12 to 23 and the lowest price is for 24 buoys and more.

With this discussion of the cork marine goods industry and its products, we have covered all the divisions and units of the cork industry concerned with the manufacture of products made wholly of cork or in which cork is a principal component part. Closely allied with the cork industry is the linoleum industry which uses cork in the form of finely pulverized powder known as cork flour. The next chapter on the linoleum industry is therefore included and this chapter will also refer further to cork carpet and cork bulletin board which were mentioned in Chapter VI on composition cork. Cork carpet and cork bulletin board are distinctly cork products, but they are made by the linoleum manufacturers on the same type of machines used in the production of linoleum.

CHAPTER IX

LINOLEUM AND CORK CARPET

LITERALLY, the linoleum industry grew out of a paint pot. The year was 1863; the paint pot stood, uncovered, in the "laboratory" of one Frederick Walton, a youthful inventor of Yorkshire, England. The same thing had happened in Walton's paint pot that happens whenever a pot of paint is left uncovered and undisturbed for a period of time. The linseed oil had come to the top and the uppermost layer in contact with the air had hardened into a tough, "rubbery" skin or film. In this film, Walton thought there must be possibilities of a new product and a great industry, although at first his ideas for its utilization were vague and indefinite.

On the English market at the time was a floor covering material made of cork and India rubber, which were ground together, mixed with certain gums and pressed out into sheets. Not entirely satisfactory, this floor covering material, called Kamptulicon, had the further disadvantage of being expensive. Here then was a possible field for the oil skin which had formed in Walton's paint pot, and which he had already begun to manufacture by "painting" linseed oil on sheets of metal and then scraping off the layers of oil skin after they had dried and hardened. Ground up and then pressed into a mass, this oxidized oil had many of the properties of India rubber. Walton combined it with finely ground cork and gums, rolled the mixture out on sheets of canvas or burlap, to increase its strength, and a brand new product was born and a new word added to the English language. For his new material, Walton coined the name "linoleum"—"linum" for flax and "oleum" for oil.[1]

In the seventy-five years since Walton invented linoleum, many changes in its manufacture, designs and use have occurred, but linoleum is still essentially the same material invented and named

[1] Walton has left a sketchy account of his invention of linoleum and his connection with the industry in a little book of recollections entitled *The Infancy and Development of Linoleum Floorcloth*, published in 1925 in London.

by Walton in 1863. He, himself, remained identified with the industry until a few years before his death in 1928, and during his later years developed and perfected a truly remarkable machine for the automatic manufacture of inlaid linoleum—the premier product of the industry. The manufacture of linoleum was begun in this country in 1873. Walton himself came over from England, bought a factory site on Staten Island, New York, built a plant, started making linoleum and named the town which grew up around the plant Linoleumville.[1]

CORK FLOUR HELPS MAKE LINOLEUM RESILIENT

The relation between the cork industry and the linoleum industry has already been indicated—cork is one of the materials of which linoleum is made, the others being linseed oil, waterproofing resins, pigments and burlap. Practically all of the burlap comes from Dundee, Scotland, which district for years has had a near monopoly in the manufacture of the special, finely woven material used in the manufacture of linoleum. The resins are principally rosin, which is the residue obtained in the distillation of turpentine, and kauri gum obtained from a species of New Zealand tree. Most of the linseed oil comes from flaxseed grown in this country, in Canada and in Argentina.

The cork used in linoleum making is the best grade of cork waste and comes principally from the stopper factories, both American and foreign. This cork waste is ground between two-ton millstones to a powder, or "flour" as it is called, so impalpably fine that it will float in the air like dust. It must be entirely free from grit or other foreign particles because the smoothness of the face of the linoleum depends largely upon the fineness and purity of the cork flour. Singularly, grinding the cork to such a powder-fine flour does not destroy its natural resiliency but seems actually to make it more resilient, and it is this characteristic of the cork which helps make linoleum a resilient flooring material.[2]

Basically, there are two different types of linoleum—plain and inlaid, and one form of inlaid—the so-called straight-line—is a

[1] The name of this town was changed in 1930 to Travis. The manufacture of linoleum at the Staten Island plant was discontinued in 1931.

[2] In the manufacture of certain linoleums of light color, wood flour is substituted for cork flour because the cork flour is brown in color and therefore cannot be used satisfactorily in making linoleum in such shades as white and light blue. Wood flour is heavier and denser than cork flour.

development of the plain. Both plain and inlaid linoleums are made in a number of different styles or forms either by variations in the manufacturing process or an additional factory operation, like printing. The following outline shows the principal different kinds of both plain and inlaid linoleum:

I. Plain Linoleum
    A. Solid color plain
    B. Printed
    C. Jaspé
II. Inlaid Linoleum
    A. Straight-line
    B. Molded

Linoleum is made in different thicknesses (called "gauges"). Current gauges are as follows: Standard (.075"); Medium (.095"); ⅛" (.125"); ³⁄₁₆" (.187") and 6 mm. (.235"). Plain linoleum is made in all of these five gauges and the last two are frequently referred to as "Battleship" linoleum. Inlaid linoleums are usually made only in the first three of these thicknesses. Thickness has little to do with production except to slow up the whole process both in actual manufacture and in seasoning. In the production of all the different kinds of linoleum in the above

Only the best grades of cork are used in the manufacture of cork flour for linoleum.

summary, except the last one—molded inlaid—the manufacturing technique is fundamentally the same.

LINOLEUM MANUFACTURE—OIL OXIDATION AND CEMENT MAKING

The first step in the manufacturing process is to get Walton's paint-pot oil skin by the oxidation of linseed oil. This was formerly done by either one of two methods—the "scrim" or the mechanical—and while these methods are not now as generally used as they once were, a brief description of them will help in explaining how linoleum is manufactured. In the scrim method, which is the oldest process, filtered linseed oil is boiled and during the boiling certain driers are added to the oil. As soon as the

Above: Interior of oxidizing shed showing scrims coated with oil.

Left: Pure oxidized linseed oil. Note how flexible and rubbery it becomes.

boiled oil is sufficiently cool, it is run over to sheds housing the scrim, which are long sheets of muslin-like cloth suspended about two inches apart. Above the rods carrying the scrims is a movable trough or tank with a perforated bottom. The boiled oil is pumped into this trough and flows through the perforations, down over the scrims. In time (six to ten weeks) the scrims become heavy, rubbery sheets of oxidized oil, half an inch thick. These sheets are then taken from the sheds, cut into pieces, ground up and are then ready for mixing with the resins.

A newer mechanical method of oxidizing the linseed oil consists of putting the raw oil mixed with the driers in a large cylindrical tank equipped with agitators. The oil absorbs oxygen from the air which is forced through the cylindrical tank and gradually stiffens into a viscous mass. By this method the oxidation is completed in so far as is practical in about 30 hours.

Right: A piece of linoleum "cement."

Below: The pile of cement on the floor has just been poured from the boiling kettle. After cooling and hardening it will be cut into chunks and put away to season.

The oxidized oil is now combined with the rosin and gums and heated in enormous kettles, in which mechanical arms keep the solution well mixed. After from two to four hours, the material becomes a spongy mass and is dumped on a clean floor. This mixture, known as "cement" or "beef," is slashed with huge knives into chunks about a foot square and a foot thick. Each batch is tested and is then put away to cure for from three to four weeks. After the curing the cement or beef is rolled out into thin sheets, which are then ground and combined with the cork flour and the pigments which give the finished linoleum its color.

Both these older methods were two-stage processes; first the oil was oxidized and then the cement was made. Linoleum cement is also made by a newer single-stage process now largely employed in the industry. In this newer process, the drying oils are oxidized in the presence of the resins to make the finished cement in the one operation.

LINOLEUM MANUFACTURE—PLAIN, JASPÉ AND PRINTED

Different types of linoleum require different proportions of cork and cement and at this point our mix looks like colored oily sawdust and also at this point the technique of making molded inlaid linoleum becomes quite different from that which produces the other kinds—plain, printed, Jaspé and straight-line inlaid.

First, the plain linoleum. Each piece of plain linoleum is of one shade only, and the color is solid all the way through to the

Front end of calendering machine showing roll of burlap to which the linoleum mix will be keyed by heated rollers.

burlap back. Our "oily-sawdust" mix goes to the calendering machines where it is fed onto the burlap and both are squeezed through heated calender rolls, the thickness of the resulting linoleum being regulated by the distance between the surfaces of the two rolls. The calendering operation forces the linoleum mix into the interstices of the burlap and keys it there. From the calendering machines, and after a rigid inspection, the linoleum goes into the "stoves" where it is hung in festoons to cure or season. These stoves are about 150 feet long, from 12 to 20 feet wide and will accommodate a festoon 90 feet in length; they are held at a temperature of about 160° F. The linoleum remains in the stoves for a period varying from a few days to several weeks depending upon weather conditions, the thickness of the linoleum and the make-up of the mix. After its seasoning is completed the linoleum is inspected again, the selvage is trimmed off and it then goes to the warehouse ready for the order which will move it out.

Jaspé linoleum has a striated, two-tone effect—the colors running in streaks or lines, roughly parallel to the length of the material. It is made exactly as is plain linoleum except that two mixes, each a different color, are fed onto the calender rolls simultaneously; the two mixes "mingle" and the striated appearance of Jaspé is the result.

Printed linoleum is simply plain linoleum with a design or pattern printed or painted on the surface. After the plain linoleum has completed its seasoning, it is taken from the stoves to the printing machines, which print the pattern or design on the ma-

[107]

Making printed linoleum.

terial by means of large flat wooden blocks. From the printing machine the linoleum goes back into the stove again, where it remains for four or five days. The mix is thus further oxidized and the paint dries thoroughly. Great care must be taken to have the color or paint of exactly the right consistency in order that it will not run or spread when fresh, and so that, when baked, it will give a hard, smooth, elastic surface which adds materially to the brilliancy and life of the linoleum.

LINOLEUM MANUFACTURE—INLAID

Inlaid linoleum as a finished product is very different from plain or printed, but one type—the straight-line inlaid—is made by using small blocks or pieces of plain linoleum. This type gets its name from the fact that each block of linoleum is cut or died out in geometrically straight lines. In one method of manufacture, these pieces of linoleum, die-cut from blankets of different colored plain linoleum, are fitted together by hand upon the burlap back. As the pieces are assembled into the finished pattern, the linoleum moves along a table to a huge hydraulic press in which the individual pieces are forced together and pushed into the burlap back so that the whole thing becomes one solid piece.

Straight-line linoleum is also made on giant rotary presses. This machine takes the linoleum mix, makes it into a blanket, cuts out the pieces, fits them together upon the burlap back, and calenders the linoleum. The material is then stoved, and, when matured, is trimmed, inspected and put in stock.

[108]

Making straight-line inlaid linoleum.

Molded inlaid linoleum is made by a very different method. Go back to the colored oily sawdust mix of oxidized oil, rosin, gums and cork flour. As many different colored batches of mix are made as are required in the finished pattern. After each color is thoroughly mixed and pulverized, it is put in a cooling room where a low temperature is maintained. In this way oxidation is not only retarded, but the colored "mix" becomes rather dry and hard, and will run or flow somewhat like sand. When sufficiently cool, the dry, sandy mix is applied to the burlap by rubbing it through metal stencils. One of these stencils is prepared for each color, there thus being required as many stencils as there are colors in the pattern.

The burlap travels along until all the colored mixes are imposed upon it, and it is then carried under a hydraulic press which sets the mix solidly and gives it a smooth even face. The plates on the press are heated so that the mix goes together and is keyed firmly to the burlap. The goods then go to the stoves and after maturing, they are taken out, trimmed, inspected rigidly, and put into the warehouse as finished stock. Considerable quantities of molded inlaid linoleum are embossed, which gives certain designs, especially tiles, the effect of hand-laid floors.

After a design in molded inlaid linoleum has been made as described above, it is then passed under great embossing presses which consist of plates fitted to particular parts of the design. As the embossing press comes down on the material, part of the design is pressed below other parts so that the tile blocks or other

[109]

Making molded inlaid linoleum.

portions of the pattern now stand out in relief—thus giving texture to the surface.

CORK CARPET—MANUFACTURE AND USE

So much for the manufacture of linoleum. Cork carpet is a calendered product but differs from linoleum in that the cork is not ground nearly so fine and the proportion of binder to cork is much smaller. It is therefore lighter than linoleum and much more resilient. It is made in $\frac{1}{4}''$ gauge only and in two solid colors—brown and green. Cork carpet goes through practically the same processes as plain linoleum, but must be handled more carefully, as it is very tender when first rolled. It is made on "unbacked" (plain) burlap. The period of stoving is not long

compared to that of linoleum due to the lightness of the mix, and cork carpet will mature in approximately ten days to two weeks. After being stoved, cork carpet is trimmed and inspected in much the same way as is linoleum.

Inspection and storage. Every single yard of linoleum is carefully inspected.

LINOLEUM AND CORK CARPET

Cork carpet is used primarily where extra resilience and quiet are desired. Such places as churches, lodges, libraries, and dens in private homes, where traffic is neither constant nor excessive, furnish the market for this material. It also provides an excellent floor for indoor tennis courts, gymnasiums and running tracks. Some special uses of cork carpet include its application on skee ball alleys and for bulletin and dart boards. As compared with linoleum, the volume manufactured is small.

CORK ALL OVER

The ceiling of this reception room of a Pennsylvania manufacturing plant is covered with acoustical cork; the walls and floor with linoleum.

GROWTH AND SIZE OF THE INDUSTRY

Prior to the establishment of a linoleum industry in this country there was an oilcloth industry dating back to 1810, and by 1859 a Government census showed fifty-six oilcloth manufacturing plants in operation in this country.[1] Prior to the Census of Manu-

[1] Floor oilcloth has been superseded by an improved material known as asphalted-felt-base floor covering made of asphalted felt on which a design is printed or painted so that when new the material resembles printed linoleum in surface appearance.

[111]

factures for 1921 much of the statistical information for the linoleum industry is combined with the data for the older oilcloth industry and it is therefore difficult to show the details of the long-time growth of the linoleum industry in this country. However, the following tabulations, which go back to 1904 as regards volume and value of linoleum manufactured, give a good indication of the economic importance of the linoleum industry for the past thirty-odd years:

LINOLEUM AND CORK CARPET

	Yards Manufactured	Dollar Value
1904	16,891,462	5,328,800
1909	30,676,254	10,844,928
1914	41,785,871	14,769,273
1919	31,932,468	27,457,045
1923	53,060,155	44,588,996
1929	48,272,133	48,744,479

	1931	1935	1937	1939
Number of Establishments..	6	4	3	4
Number of Workers	2,895	3,718	5,269	4,446
Wages and Salaries Paid..$	3,595,333	$ 4,643,991	$ 7,522,571	$ 6,751,772
Materials Manufactured:				
Value Linoleum	$19,163,840	$18,099,259	$29,197,938	$29,104,469
Yards Linoleum	20,125,317	24,237,371	35,377,434	35,686,413
Value Cork Carpet	$243,898	$189,459	$376,436	$328,427
Yards Cork Carpet	246,754	215,318	367,221	318,372

A linoleum floor in a modern dining room.
The color scheme is eggplant purple and silver.

LINOLEUM AND CORK CARPET

Like all building material industries, the linoleum industry was particularly hard hit by the economic depression which set in in 1929 due largely to the collapse in new building and home construction. By 1935, however, the industry was "coming back" vigorously. As the construction industry revives and especially as new homes are built and older homes renovated, the linoleum industry will continue this come-back so that the decade ahead of it may be the largest in its history.

LINOLEUM "COMES OUT OF THE KITCHEN"

One of the most striking features in the whole development of the linoleum industry is the way in which its use has been extended. Not so many years ago, linoleum was considered a suitable floor covering material only for kitchens and bathrooms and it was usually installed simply by spreading it over the floor or by tacking it down. Today linoleum is used as a floor covering for every room in the house, aboard ships, in all types of office and public buildings, and in addition is used on the tops of tables, counters and desks, in railway cars, buses and in airplanes.

Several factors account for this extension in the use of linoleum, especially as a floor covering. To an increasing extent the durability and the sanitary character of the material have been recog-

*A custom-built linoleum floor
in the reception room of a radio broadcasting studio.*   [113]

nized; the drab and uninteresting patterns formerly manufactured have been superseded by modern designs and color combinations created by artists; and, finally, linoleum is now expertly installed over a layer of lining felt so as to make a really comfortable, resilient and permanent floor.

Linoleum is sold by the manufacturers to wholesalers, who in turn distribute the product to the retailers who sell it to the ultimate buyers. Many of these retailers are flooring material shops exclusively, but most of them are department or furniture stores. Linoleum is sold by the manufacturers in rolls 6 feet wide and approximately 90 feet long and usually remains in full length rolls until cut up for the ultimate purchaser. The usual pricing unit is the square yard. A housewife or other purchaser may buy the material and lay it or have it laid herself but very often in the case of both large and small installations, the purchaser buys the linoleum and has it laid by the dealer. Many wholesalers and most retailers are flooring contractors and take an order for a given quantity of linoleum and an equivalent quantity of lining felt to be used under the linoleum, both to be cemented to the floor with a special adhesive which has been developed for this particular purpose.

Linoleum is also sold by the manufacturers to other manufacturers making desks, tables, kitchen equipment, counters, file cabinets and various other kinds of equipment which are furnished with a linoleum top by the manufacturers.

A custom-built linoleum floor
in the salesroom of a clock manufacturer.

CHAPTER X

MISCELLANEOUS—CONCLUSIONS

WE have now covered the cork industry. The oak-tree bark with which we started has been transformed into an almost endless variety of finished products. To these we shall add three others—cork brick, insulating fire brick and cork ingot insulation.[1] The last two are interesting "contradictions."

Cork bricks are used principally as a flooring material in barns and stables and other buildings where live stock is kept. Cork bricks are made of finely granulated cork and refined asphalt, thoroughly mixed while hot, and then compressed and molded into brick form in three thicknesses—2″, 1¾″ and 1″. The standard area dimensions are 9″ x 4″.

Cork bricks are widely used as an ideal flooring material for barns and stables because of several of the physical properties possessed by natural cork which were discussed in Chapter I. First, because of the natural compressibility and resilience of cork, a cork brick floor is a highly resilient floor and therefore a very comfortable floor for the animals to stand on. This property of resilience means that less bedding can be used with a cork brick floor than with other types of flooring and this means for greater sanitation in the buildings and stalls in which such bricks are used. Second, because of the natural resistance of cork to the penetration of liquids, increased greatly in the case of cork brick by the addition of asphalt, a cork brick floor is highly nonabsorbent and can be readily cleaned and washed, thus resulting in a highly sanitary floor. Third, cork bricks make a decidedly non-slippery floor because of the high coefficient of friction possessed by natural cork discussed in Chapter I. This is one of the most important properties accounting for the use of cork brick in barns and stables; a floor on which the animals can slip is a decidedly dangerous and expensive floor especially when it is considered that a broken leg may

---

[1] Spanish black is also a cork product. It is a very fine, dead-black powder used as a pigment and is made by charring or calcining natural cork.

A modern cow barn floored with cork brick.

mean the destruction of a valuable animal. A cork brick floor is non-slippery even when wet. Finally, because of the low thermal conductivity of cork, a cork brick floor makes a warm floor for the animals to lie on and barns floored with cork brick can be kept at more healthy temperatures than if the floors were covered with a "cold" material.

The insulating fire brick mentioned above is a striking illustration, even though a somewhat extreme one, of the versatility of cork. Repeated references in earlier chapters and the whole of Chapter V have emphasized the use of cork as a low-temperature or cold insulator. Insulating fire brick made with the use of cork is the complete opposite—it is a heat insulator used either directly exposed or as a back-up insulation behind the fire brick lining in the walls of furnaces and firing chambers in which temperatures from 1,600° F. to 2,600° F. are used. In making these insulating

The 200-inch telescope mirror for the California Institute of Technology was made in this oven made of cork insulating fire brick.

fire bricks finely ground cork is combined with the brick mix which consists of various earths and clays. After being molded, the bricks are fired at very high temperatures and at these temperatures, the fine particles of cork are burned out. The spaces they occupied in the mix are now voids within the earth and clay mixture and the resulting bricks are excellent insulators at high temperatures.

Making cork insulating fire brick.

Cork ingot insulation is one of the most recent developments of the industry. Made of finely-ground cork completely plated with a ceramic coating, this material is shoveled or thrown directly on top of the molten metal in a freshly-poured ingot mold. When steel from the open hearth is poured into the molds to form ingots, the molten steel immediately begins to cool and solidify. This results in the steel's contracting and as the portion of the molten steel which is adjacent to the mold solidifies first, a cavity occurs in the

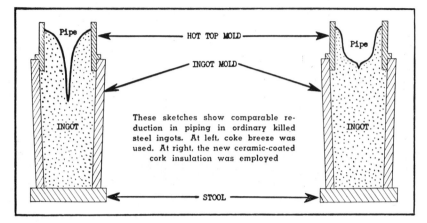

HOT TOP MOLD

Pipe

Pipe

INGOT MOLD

INGOT

INGOT

These sketches show comparable reduction in piping in ordinary killed steel ingots. At left, coke breeze was used. At right, the new ceramic-coated cork insulation was employed

STOOL

middle of the ingot at the top and is termed the "pipe." Inasmuch as the top portion of the ingot (called the crop end) has to be cut off to the bottom of the pipe, it is essential that the metal in the top of the ingot remain molten sufficiently long to feed the molten metal in to fill this pipe or cavity so as to reduce its length in order to increase the yield per ingot. The sketches above show how wasteful

[118]

Pouring 32,000 pound steel ingots.

a deep pipe is and indicate the saving resulting from the use of cork insulation.

A four- to six-inch layer of cork ingot insulation on a 4,000-lb. ingot will keep the metal in the top of the mold molten for approximately $1\frac{1}{4}$ hours as compared with fifteen to twenty minutes for coke breeze, one of several other materials which have been used for ingot insulation. Of several advantages resulting from the use of cork ingot insulation the most important are higher yield per ingot and better regulation of ingot size, both highly important factors in steel production.

CORK AND LINOLEUM—PRODUCTION

In the various product chapters, the size of each division of the cork industry on the basis of value of products manufactured was indicated. These data came principally from the United States Census of Manufactures and are combined in the table below for the year 1939, the latest for which census data are available.

AMERICAN CORK AND LINOLEUM INDUSTRIES
1939 [1]

	Linoleum	Cork
Number of establishments	4	35
Number of workers (average for year)	4,446	3,265
Wages and salaries paid	$ 6,751,772	$ 3,932,870
Cost of materials, fuel and purchased electricity	14,384,022	8,412,294
Value of products manufactured	37,405,785	17,723,584
Value added by manufacture	23,021,763	9,311,290
Linoleum—plain and printed	$ 7,519,238	
—inlaid	21,585,231	
Cork carpet	328,427	
Cork stoppers		$ 3,184,049
Other natural cork products		1,644,514
Cork insulation and pipe covering		5,901,699
Ground and granulated cork and waste		1,272,946
Composition cork gaskets, discs, washers, etc.		3,146,375
All other composition cork products		1,853,492
Cork tile		219,958
Life preservers, blocks and floats		354,481
Total values—linoleum and cork products	$29,432,896	$17,577,514
Products other than linoleum and cork	7,972,889	1,242,863
Total values of all products as per Government Census	$37,405,785	$18,820,377
Less value of cork products made by other industries		1,096,793
Cork industry—total value of all products manufactured		$17,723,584

Combined, these two American industries, based wholly or in part on cork, show a total product value of well over $50,000,000. Neither has had the spectacular growth of some American industries, but the present size and importance of each is largely the product of the past forty years, witness the fact that in 1900 the product value of each was less than $5,000,000.

[1] The cork insulation and pipe covering value in this table does not check with the 1939 value for insulation products shown on p. 66, because of an author's adjustment by which $200,000 of the ground and granulated cork and waste value in this table is included in the insulation products value, increasing this from $5,901,699 to $6,100,000. The balance of the granulated and waste value reported in the table above is evidently blocker waste, shavings and scrap.

CORK AND LINOLEUM—IMPORTS AND EXPORTS

The plant and productive capacities of the American cork and linoleum industries are adequate to meet this country's requirements fully in the case of all products with the possible exception of cork paper. Furthermore, all manufactured cork products are dutiable at various rates under Paragraph 1511 of the Tariff Act of 1930. Therefore, as shown in the tabulation below, except for cork paper and a considerable volume of cork stoppers, recent imports of foreign-made manufactured cork products into this country have not been very large.

UNITED STATES IMPORTS—CORK MANUFACTURES AND LINOLEUM

[Thousand Dollars]

	1933	1934	1935	1936	1937	1938	1939	1940
Cork discs	103.9	108.9	45.9	60.0	69.4	48.5	42.0	55.9
Cork insulation and pipe covering	19.6	8.7	5.1	1.2	76.4	1.2	1.1	.3
Stoppers and shell corks	179.6	407.1	170.4	196.5	214.3	138.6	194.4	361.0
Cork squares	3.0	44.3	37.3	44.8	19.2	4.0	2.1	2.6
Cork paper	41.4	250.6	317.2	398.9	167.2	123.6	34.8	5.7
Other cork manufactures	17.3	9.0	66.7	71.9	71.3	51.7	43.6	35.5
Linoleum and cork carpet	307.1	340.4	609.5	437.1	675.2	246.4	344.5	200.2

Due largely to the fact that manufacturing costs, especially wages, are much lower in foreign countries than in the United States, the American cork and linoleum industries have been able to develop only a very limited export business in manufactured cork products. This is shown by the following table.

UNITED STATES EXPORTS—CORK MANUFACTURES AND LINOLEUM

[Thousand Dollars]

	1933	1934	1935	1936	1937	1938	1939	1940
Cork discs, washers and wafers	248.6	289.9	267.9	191.0	321.6	227.0	407.0	393.5
Cork stoppers	34.3	39.3	42.4	90.3	105.3	73.6	123.0	205.5
Other cork manufactures	161.9	215.9	241.8	321.0	414.5	403.2	557.3	742.8
Linoleum	55.2	87.8	99.0	103.6	151.3	137.9	171.8	218.3

The bulk of this export business is done with Canada and other units of the British Empire, with Cuba, various South American countries and the Philippine Islands, but occasional shipments of American-made cork products go to the far corners of the world.

"WRITE A BETTER BOOK, BUILD A BETTER MOUSETRAP . . ."

Built on a product of Nature remarkable for its distinctive physical properties, the American cork industry is itself remarkable and distinctive. Every pound of its raw material is of foreign origin and has to be imported into this country. For some 2,000 years this raw material has been known and used and has been an article of commerce. But up until less than fifty years ago this raw material remained a simple forestry product with its uses confined to bottle stoppers, simple specialty products and a few articles for marine use. For some 2,000 years, in other words, the cork-producing countries of Europe and Africa, in whose national economy cork is a most important factor, made little progress in the development of new uses for the material with which Nature has endowed them with a monopoly.

Down to the end of the nineteenth century, the cork industry was essentially still the simple cork-cutting industry which had been started shortly before the end of the economic Middle Ages. That this is not the case today is due in part to the inventive genius of Americans and to the research work of the American industry. The late 1890's brought the beginning of the cork insulation industry based on an American discovery and invention. A few years later, the cork tile industry was founded in this country and provided a market for the valuable shavings resulting from the tapering of corks. By 1910, American research had contributed to the foundation of the composition cork industry, and concurrently with these three major developments, the American industry pioneered in the development of other important cork products, including brick, isolation and acoustical corkboard, and in adapting the material to innumerable specific uses throughout industry and as an integral part in hundreds of articles of common usage.

It may be said that if all of this had not been done in this country it would have been done elsewhere. This may be so, and other countries, notably England and Germany, have contributed to the development of the modern cork industry and have helped make this industry more than a simple cork-cutting business. And there is another important aspect to this. Repeatedly in the product chapters of this book, references were made to substitutes for cork. Cork stoppers have their substitutes; cork insulation has its competitors, so does cork composition and so do cork tile and marine goods. Often the competitors and the substitutes are less expensive, and if price is the first or only consideration cork may lose out, for while it is an economical material, it is not a cheap material. To hold its market, therefore, the cork industry cannot sit back and let the superiority of its product speak for itself. In modern business competition products speak in very hushed voices as compared with the voices of the competitors themselves. And so, while it may be true that if you write a better book or build a better mousetrap, the world will make a beaten path to your door, the world does so only after it knows about your book or your mousetrap—or your cork.

[122]

Photo courtesy Junta Nacional da Cortica

Somewhere in Portugal, this fine cork oak in its prime is shown being stripped of some 500 pounds of high quality cork which will be manufactured into a wide variety of products ranging from the humble cork stopper to vital parts in a dive bomber.

APPENDICES

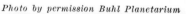

Photo by permission Buhl Planetarium

A peace-time use of cork as insulation on the brine-cooling equipment and ducts of the air-conditioning system in the Buhl Planetarium in Pittsburgh. Some of this aluminum-painted cork insulation may have come from the tree in Portugal shown opposite.

The new National Gallery of Art in Washington opened
March 18, 1941. A half million board feet of corkboard and
25,000 square feet of cork tile were used in the construction
of this magnificent building.

APPENDIX A

A THOUSAND USES OF CORK

A T the end of Chapter III, reference was made to the almost endless variety of products into which the bark of the cork oak is converted. The various product chapters in this book grouped these manufactured cork products according to divisions of the industry producing them. The following descriptive listing is a sort of catalogue of finished cork products based on type of service and indicates both the versatility of cork and the degree to which its use has been extended during the past forty years.

AUTOMOTIVE AND TRANSPORTATION

 *Automobiles.* Cork gaskets are widely used in automotive engine construction wherever low pressure and low temperature conditions are encountered. Typical examples are oil pan gaskets, valve cover plate gaskets, timing gear cover gaskets. Cork seals are frequently used to retain lubricant in the crank shaft bearings and to exclude dirt.

Cork gaskets are used as cushions and dust seals in the assembly of instrument panels.

Natural cork floats are used in carburetors, and also to actuate gasoline and oil level gauges.

Certain automobile manufacturers employ natural cork inserts in their clutch plates. These clutches run in oil to give smooth engagement of the clutch and to dissipate frictional heat.

Cork in the form of gaskets, seals, packings, etc., is widely used in many automobile parts and accessories such as headlamps, rear axles, and fuel pumps and strainers.

Automobile truck bodies handling perishable goods are frequently insulated with corkboard to preserve proper temperature conditions.

Railway Cars. Corkboard is used to insulate refrigerator cars. It is also used in air-conditioned passenger cars for insulating ducts and brine tanks.

A special material known as corkbase is used to form the sub-floors in many of the modern lightweight streamline trains.

Aircraft. Cork sheets (or ground cork mixed with a suitable adhesive) are used to form a non-slip tread on wing walks. The cabin floors of many airliners are covered with a light-weight cork material.

Certain airplane engines use cork push-rod housing packings and rocker arm cover gaskets. Cork is also found at various points in the fuel and lubrication systems.

Hydroplane floats are frequently constructed with cork nose bumpers.

Marine. Cork has long been a standard material from which life preservers and ring buoys are made.

Every yacht harbor will display a generous assortment of cork mooring buoys and fenders.

MUSICAL INSTRUMENTS

Pipe Organs. Cork is used in pipe organs in the form of gaskets for wind chests, and as friction strips for the tuning plugs.

Wind Instruments. High grade natural cork is used to form valve cushions and tight joints in various wind instruments, and cork strips are applied to mutes to give them a firm yet easy fit, which depends upon friction alone.

Miscellaneous. Cork is frequently used to form baton grips, and some of the larger drum sticks are made with a natural cork center or core.

ELECTRICAL EQUIPMENT

Cork gaskets are used to prevent leakage and contamination of the liquids employed in electrical transformers, circuit breakers, lightning arresters, and other transmission equipment. They are also used as dust seals in meters. In electric motors and generators are frequently found cork oil retainers and end-play bumpers.

Cork gaskets are used in conduit fittings and cork plugs are helpful in protecting open conduits during construction.

Cork machinery isolation is used under transformers, motors and generators, and other vibrating equipment.

FOOD MACHINERY AND EQUIPMENT

Food preparation machinery frequently uses cork insulation in such varied types of equipment as dough-mixers and quick-freez- ing apparatus for the preservation of meats and vegetables.

Natural cork strips have long been used to form gaskets for the tops of butter churns.

As in practically every other type of machine where there is a problem of keeping oil in its place, cork gaskets are widely used in connection with such parts as gear cases and hand-hole covers.

GLASS MACHINERY AND EQUIPMENT

Cork composition wheels are used for polishing the edges and bevels of plate glass and mirrors. They are also used for removing excess sealing compound from the edges of laminated safety glass. Cork wheels are also used in the pottery industry for polishing and touching up defects.

HOUSEHOLD EQUIPMENT

Flooring. Cork flour is used in the manufacture of linoleum and cork tile makes one of the finest floors available.

Refrigerators. Some of the better refrigerator boxes are insulated with corkboard. In the mechanism of many electrical refrigerators are found cork gaskets, packings, and other parts such as spacers and outlet plugs which support the tubing through which the refrigerant is circulated. In larger installations cork may be used as a vibration-deadening mounting.

 *Washing Machines.* Gaskets of cork are used for gear cases, cover plates, etc. Cork rings are used as oil retainers on drive shafts, wringer control shafts, and elsewhere. Cork gaskets are used to prevent chipping of the porcelain finish where legs and other external parts are attached.

Miscellaneous. Cork composition handles have been used on electric irons.

Cork composition sheets are widely used in making up novelty table mats and coasters, also waste baskets and the like.

Cork is used as a facing on metal embroidery hoops.

MEASURING, HANDLING, AND DISPENSING OF GASES & LIQUIDS

Gauges. Cork gaskets are used as seals and to cushion the assembly of metal and glass parts. Cork floats are frequently used in connection with the indicator mechanism of gauges which show the level of a liquid in a tank.

Meters. Cork stuffing box packings and gaskets are found in fuel, water, and gas meters.

Containers. Cork gaskets are used on open-head steel drums, especially when the contents of the drum are oils or food products which might be affected or contaminated by other less neutral gasket materials. Carboys are often stoppered with a cork and are cushioned against shocks in transit by the use of cork blocks or specially molded composition.

Gasoline Dispensing Pumps. In this familiar equipment, cork is used to cushion and seal the glass parts of various visible flow devices. Cork gaskets are also used in the pump and meter mechanisms, and a cork disc is an important part in many nozzle valves.

Truck Tanks. Many of these are insulated with corkboard, and cork gaskets and valve discs are found in the discharge valves.

TEXTILE MACHINERY AND EQUIPMENT

Cork cots are used in spinning cotton, worsted, and silk yarns.

Cork is used on loom take-up rolls, clutches, and brake bands. There are similar uses for the material on other textile machinery such as measuring machines and warpers.

Corkboard is used to insulate textile mill roofs to help preserve proper atmospheric conditions and to prevent condensation.

LUBRICATING EQUIPMENT AND BEARINGS

Because it remains unaffected by oils and greases, cork is widely used for gaskets and packings in grease guns, oil cups, sight feed oilers, and other types of lubricating equipment and devices.

Composition cork, specially treated, in the form of gaskets and rings, is used as an oil and grease retainer in bearings on engines, motors, machines, railroad car trucks and similar mechanical equipment.

OFFICE AND STORE EQUIPMENT

Corkboard is used to insulate refrigerated show cases.

Typewriters are frequently mounted on cork pads for deadening noise and vibration. Typewriters intended for stencil cutting are provided with cork composition feed rolls which are not affected by oils or chemicals present in the stencil paper.

Cork blocks wedged into hollow sections of metal furniture are effective in deadening resonance.

Cork carpet makes the finest bulletin boards, and cork sheets are used to make a non-slip bottom for file drawers.

PACKAGING EQUIPMENT AND MATERIALS

Wrapping Machines. Cork-covered tension and feed rolls are used on many wrapping machines handling waxed paper, cellophane, and similar materials.

Bottles and Containers. For centuries natural cork has been made into bottle stoppers and now screw caps and crowns are made with cork liners. Cork discs are used in the caps of tubes containing tooth paste, cold cream, and similar preparations.

Packing for Shipment. Cork is used for spacing, cushioning, and insulating numerous articles and materials during shipment.

PLUMBING, HEATING, COOLING AND VENTILATING

 Cold Storage. Corkboard is the standard low-temperature insulating material used in cold storage warehouses, ice houses, fruit storages and all similar buildings.

Cold Lines. Cork pipe covering is used to insulate cold lines and to prevent "sweating."

Pipe Fittings. Cork is used in various types of thread protectors for valves, fittings, and pipe ends.

Oil Burners. Many oil burners employ cork gaskets and floats, as well as cork vibration dampening mountings.

Building Insulation. To obtain maximum economy and efficiency from heating and air-conditioning systems, buildings and homes must be insulated, and cork is widely used for this service. In the case of air-conditioning, corkboard is also used for insulating ducts, and the circulating and cooling mechanism is often mounted on cork to reduce vibration.

SCIENTIFIC INSTRUMENTS AND EQUIPMENT

Chemical Laboratories. Cork rings are used as rests for round-bottom flasks.

Entomological Equipment. Cork sheets faced with glazed white paper are used to mount and display entomological specimens.

Testing Laboratories and Rooms. Laboratories and test rooms must frequently be maintained at constant temperature. Such rooms are usually insulated with corkboard.

Miscellaneous. Cork blocks are used as a surface upon which dissections may be performed. Cork spacers and stoppers are used in glass tubes for packaging photographic chemicals, and certain kinds of forceps are faced with cork.

SPORTING GOODS AND TOYS

Baseball. Cork centers are used in official major league baseballs and in balls manufactured for indoor baseball.

Beach Sports. Novelty sandals and bracelets, beads, and other items for beach use are made entirely or partially of cork. Life-line floats for beaches and swimming pools are made of cork.

Fishing. In this field, cork serves in the form of fishing rod handles, floats and bobbers, artificial bait bodies, and as a lining for tackle boxes.

Golf. Many golf club handles are made with an underwrapping of cork.

Miscellaneous. Other sport and game uses for cork include its use in making badminton shuttlecocks and table tennis racquets and as a facing for dart and backgammon boards. Most of the whistles used by game officials have a small cork ball in them.

MISCELLANEOUS USES AND APPLICATIONS

Artificial Fingers. Cork has been used in making artificial fingers, but contrary to popular belief "cork" legs are not made from cork.

Artillery. Plugs made of insulation and composition cork are used in making artillery shells.

Barns. Cork bricks make the finest kind of flooring in live stock barns and stables.

Dies. Cork strips are used as push-outs in dies used for making paper boxes.

Furnaces. Cork is used in making insulating fire brick for furnace linings.

Glazing. Cork strips are sometimes used to make a cushion and seal in metal window frames, such as are used in basements and greenhouse construction.

Imitation Leather. Finely ground cork applied to fabric with a suitable adhesive or binder and further processed according to the results desired can be made to imitate closely the appearance of suède or other types of leathers.

Ladders. To prevent slipping on uncertain surfaces, ladders are frequently provided with cork feet.

Movies. In making sound movies cork is often used on "gravel" paths instead of stone gravel which crunches and makes the dialogue hard to understand.

Sanding. Cork blocks are used as a support for sandpaper or emery cloth in the hand sanding of such things as wood molding.

Shoes. Many shoes are manufactured with cork inner soles, box toes, counters, and bottom filler. Various orthopedic appliances such as arch supports employ cork pads. Blocks of natural cork, called "lame-lifts," are used in the construction of special shoes to compensate for one leg being shorter than the other.

Tobacco. Cork is used for making tips and mouthpieces for cigars and cigarettes.

Valves. Natural cork seats are used in the foot valves of small hand-operated pumps used on blow torches and camp stoves.

Watches. Cork discs are used to replace the expensive and fragile movements in sample watch cases carried by salesmen.

Miscellaneous Machinery. Power lawn-mowers employ cork gaskets, carburetor floats, and oil retainers, and some are equipped with cork clutch facings. Certain types of industrial sewing machines use a cork friction drive. Some floor-polishing machines use cork pulleys to give a positive drive.

Composition cork is used in mat form in the printing of newspapers, as a between-joints material in road building and in the manufacture of various specialties ranging from bath mats and waste baskets to women's hat ornaments.

APPENDIX B

LOW TEMPERATURE INSULATION

HEAT is now generally recognized as a form of energy with a natural and most insistent tendency to move or "flow" from areas or objects of higher temperature to areas or objects of lower temperature. In this tendency heat shows the same characteristic as unconfined water, forever seeking common levels, or, as it is called in the case of heat flow, temperature equilibrium. In fact, it was this marked similarity in the action of heat and water which accounted for one of the early theories of heat which held that it was an invisible, elastic and weightless fluid, called *caloric*, that accounted for all thermal phenomena by moving in and out of gases, liquids and solids in some mysterious manner and even combining with them temporarily. But this theory gave way almost a century ago to the modern kinetic-molecular theory which holds heat to be a form of energy.

In its natural and persistent tendency to secure and maintain temperature equilibrium this energy is transferred or transmitted from one place to another by three distinct processes.

1. *Conduction.* By this process heat is transferred by and through matter without any visible motion in the matter itself. A common every-day evidence of heat transfer by conduction is seen in the way in which the handle of a silver spoon heats up when the bowl end is put into a cup of hot soup or coffee.

2. *Convection.* This is the process by which heat is transferred by the motion of heated matter such as air and water. The flow of heat from a warm room to a cold room and the circulation of heated water in a hot water system are evidences of heat transfer by convection.

3. *Radiation.* By this process heat is transmitted without the aid of matter by wave motion through the ether just as light is transmitted. The most common evidence of heat transmission by radiation is seen in the way in which the heat from the sun reaches the earth.

These three heat transmitting processes are forever at work to bring about temperature equilibrium, and to prevent them from accomplishing their purpose in the low-temperature and cold storage fields, an insulating barrier, like a solid wall of corkboard, is built around boxes, rooms and whole buildings, and cold pipe lines are surrounded with cork covering. Economically, the problem of maintaining low temperatures has long been much more difficult and expensive than the problem of maintaining higher temperatures. Homes and buildings generally, for example, for centuries have been heated in cold weather, more or less efficiently to be sure, but it is only recently that the problem of cooling such buildings in summer is being met. More and more in the future the efficient and economical cooling of these buildings will call for increasing quantities of low-temperature insulation, but today the big market for efficient low-temperature insulation is in the cold storage field. Prior to the development of cork insulation many different materials and various types of construction were used for the low-temperature insulation so necessary in cold storage work. Sawdust, shavings, hay, cottonseed hulls, cinders and charcoal and various fibrous mineral products such as mineral wool and slag wool—all have been used for insulating the walls and ceilings of ice houses, brewers' cellars and cold storage rooms and

buildings. These are all known as "fill" materials because they were used by packing them in to fill a space between an outer and an inner wall, and although occasionally still used, the day of these fill materials is largely past due primarily to the development of corkboard—a structural material of much greater efficiency.

THERMAL CONDUCTIV-
ITY TESTING EQUIP-
MENT

These pictures show the hot-plate equipment used in determining the k values of insulation materials. The upper photograph shows corkboard under test.

As indicated in Chapter V, modern corkboard was discovered and patented in 1892, and has been the standard low-temperature insulating material for the past forty years. These same forty years have also seen the invention and development of other insulators which have come on the market as substitutes or competitors of corkboard. Most of these competitive materials are cheaper than corkboard, and often, therefore, an installation using one of these competing materials may show a lower first cost than will a comparable installation of corkboard. Cooling and refrigerating are expensive processes, and in the low-temperature insulation field, first cost is often the least important cost of an installation which is to be in constant service for, say, twenty-five or thirty years. It is the operating cost of the installation which goes on year after year that ultimately is of much greater importance than first cost. Various factors, of course, affect this operating cost, but one of the most important is the efficiency and performance of the insulating material used in the installation.

I. PHYSICAL PROPERTIES TEST DATA

In order to determine the relative efficiency and performance of a number of substitute insulators as compared with corkboard, the Cork Insulation Manufacturers Association (a division of the Cork Institute of America) recently commissioned two well-known testing Laboratories, Pittsburgh Testing Laboratory and the Engineering Experiment Station of Pennsylvania State College, to make an extensive series of tests on corkboard and five substitute non-cork insulators sold for low-temperature service. In addition to the basic testing for thermal conductivity, the tests also covered moisture absorption, fire hazard, and various structural properties. It

CORKBOARD—AFTER AND BEFORE FIRE TEST
Notice that the flame pitted the surface of the board but did not burn through.

will be impossible here to go into the results of all the testing by the two Laboratories, but the following brief summary of the results of the thermal conductivity testing and of the fire testing are indicative of the reason for corkboard being the standard low-temperature insulating material.

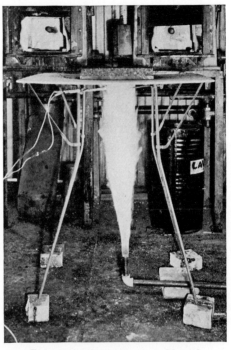

Fire test under way on corkboard specimen.

The insulating effectiveness of a material depends basically upon what is called the thermal conductivity of the insulator. This is an inherent property of a material based on a measurement of the amount of heat which will flow through the material.[1] Thermal conductivity ("k") is measured and stated as a coefficient in the form of a two or three place decimal fraction and the lower the value of this coefficient the smaller the heat transfer through the material and the greater its insulating efficiency. The results of the Association's thermal conductivity testing at one of the three mean temperatures used (60° F.) are shown in the table on the following page; the greater efficiency of corkboard is indicated by the percentage ratings of the substitute non-cork materials.

The fire testing was done in accordance with a method approved by the United States Bureau of Standards for such testing on a

[1] Thermal conductivity in this country is ordinarily expressed in B.t.u., per hour, per square foot, per inch thickness, per degree F. temperature difference between the two surfaces of the material. A B.t.u. (British thermal unit) is the amount of heat required to raise the temperature of one pound of water 1° F. The definition just stated is correctly written:

$$\frac{\text{B.t.u.}}{(\text{hr.})\ (\text{sq. ft.})\ \dfrac{\text{deg. F.}}{\text{in.}}} = \frac{\text{B.t.u. (in.)}}{(\text{hr.})\ (\text{sq. ft.})\ (\text{deg. F.})}$$

similar material. Each specimen was in the test for a period of 20 minutes during which the temperature was raised from room temperature to 1,450° F. All of the materials except corkboard were either completely consumed in the fire test, except for an ash residue, or the binder in the material burned out. In none of the tests on corkboard did the flame break through the specimen and burning ceased within one minute after the flame was shut off. Approximately 70% of the weight of the corkboard specimen was left at the end of the fire test and the corkboard was described as "fire retardant" while all of the other non-cork materials were classified as "combustible."

RESULTS OF THERMAL CONDUCTIVITY TESTS—DRY MATERIALS

Insulation	Thermal Conductivity (k) 60° F. Mean Temperature		Relative Insulating Value Corkboard = 100	
	PSC	PTL	PSC	PTL
CORKBOARD *	0.277	0.270	100.	100.
Shredded Redwood Bark	0.294	0.279	94.6	96.8
Animal Hair Board	0.315	0.288	88.3	93.8
Wood Fiber Board	0.322	0.302	86.3	89.4
Mineral Wool Board	0.324	0.318	85.8	84.9
Vegetable Fiber Board	0.356	0.336	78.1	80.4

* Corkboard values are averages of values for boards of five different manufacturers. The initials in the value columns stand for the names of the Laboratories— Pennsylvania State College and Pittsburgh Testing Laboratory.

II. TESTING UNDER SIMULATED USAGE CONDITIONS

The physical properties testing described above determined comparable values for the various materials by recognized scientific methods and under laboratory conditions. But between such laboratory-controlled tests and actual usage in the low-temperature insulation field there is one great difference which the testing described above did not and could not include in the data reported. This great difference results from the fact that in actual service every low-temperature insulating barrier is subject to a greater or lesser degree to powerful forces seeking to drive moisture into the insulation. As these forces succeed they reduce or destroy the effectiveness of the insulation because water is an excellent conductor of heat. In order to determine the relative insulating effectiveness of corkboard and a number of non-cork materials offered for low-temperature insulation service, the Cork Insulation Manufacturers Association in 1937 commissioned the Engineering Experiment Station of The Pennsylvania State College to carry out a test program in which the insulating materials would be subjected to conditions approaching those encountered in actual service as closely as possible. This program lasted almost three years and is the most comprehensive attempt to date to measure low-temperature insulating effectiveness under service conditions. A brief summary of the results of some of the tests taken from the complete report published by the Association (*Low Temperature Insulation— Simulated Usage Test Data, 1940*) will be given here. First, however, a short discussion of the methods by which moisture destroys insulating effectiveness and a brief description of the testing plan.

The problem of moisture in low-temperature insulation is not created because someone washes down or turns a hose on the insulated barrier although obviously water from any source has its effect. But entirely without any washing or hosing we would have our moisture problem for the reason that the air in which we live and work contains moisture. This moisture content of the air varies greatly as between localities, seasons of the year and from day to day in the same place and season, and under the proper conditions this atmospheric moisture becomes water because of one of Nature's phenomena—the dew-point temperature.

The most common evidence of the dew-point temperature is the clean, sparkling dew with which the whole countryside is so often covered in the morning. But this same phenomenon accounts for the "steaming" of windows, for the "sweating" of walls and for the film of moisture which forms on a glass of ice water in a warm room. The dew-point temperature varies with the temperature and moisture content of the air and can be defined as that temperature at which the air is fully saturated by the vapor present and below which some of this vapor is precipitated or condensed. In every

[137]

The phenomenon of the dew point in a cold-storage room

low-temperature installation we have vapor being condensed into water because at some point in every such installation the temperature is below the dew point. One of the worst places for this condensation to occur—and one of the most common—is within the insulation itself.

To these two "devils"—atmospheric moisture and the dew-point temperature—in the field of low-temperature insulation we add a third—Nature's abhorrence of an unbalanced condition. With these three "devils" Nature sets in to weaken or ruin the insulating barrier the day it is put in service by driving moisture into it. It will be impossible here to describe completely the process and methods by which Nature does this, but here is a brief description of the process as it results from the action of the moisture-penetrating force called vapor-pressure differential.

In any air-filled area, the air and its moisture content exert a definite measurable pressure. Warm air can hold a much higher moisture content than can cold air, and because of this the vapor pressure on the outside of a cold room will ordinarily be considerably greater than the vapor pressure within the room. In a milk room, for example, held at 32° F. and with a relative humidity of 100%—saturation—the vapor pressure within such a room, tightly closed, would be 0.0886 pounds per square inch. If, on the other side of the insulated wall of this room we have an atmosphere of, say, 70° F. and 80% humidity we would have a vapor pres-

Three boxes in test position ready for their tops. Note truck-scale used for weighing.

sure of 0.2902 pounds per square inch. The difference between these two pressures—0.2016 pounds per square inch or almost 30 pounds per square foot—is the force of the vapor pressure differential driving or carrying moisture into the insulating barrier in order to equalize the vapor pressure within and without the room.

So much for the service conditions which account for this testing program. The test units—twenty altogether—were 3-foot sealed boxes, each built to imitate a small cold-storage room. On the floor of each box there was a 10-gallon water pan, each containing an electrical heating unit which automatically held the temperature within the box at a predetermined value. Being submerged in the water, the heating element vaporized some of the water so that in all probability the atmosphere within each box was like a dense warm fog. The temperature of this fog within the boxes was 90° F. in some cases and 100° F. in others. The boxes were installed in a cold room in which the temperature was varied from 20° F. down to −4° F. Such were the conditions which created the vapor-pressure differential within and without the box and such were [139]

the conditions under which moisture was driven into the insulation. Periodically, the boxes were drained and weighed to measure how much moisture each had absorbed; individual box meters measured the electric power consumed by each box to maintain the temperature differential within and without it.

The boxes were tested in several series, and with different types of surface finish. The first series of five boxes (one cork box and four non-cork boxes) was under test the shortest period of time—19 weeks. Another series of three boxes (one cork and two non-cork) remained under test over two years—108 weeks. As indicated above the test values are in terms of water absorbed and watt hours of electricity consumed. The following table

A non-cork box begins to fail.
Moisture, driven into the sides, has drained into the bottom, leaked out around the drain and frozen.

summarizes the test results on the first series of five boxes mentioned above; a full report on these boxes and all the others is contained in the Association's publication.

POWER CONSUMPTION AND WATER ABSORBED
BOXES WITH NO SURFACE PROTECTION ON HOT SIDE

(NC used in column headings stands for Non-cork.)

	Box No.				
WEEKS	Cork A	NC 1	NC 2	NC 3	NC 4
AVERAGE DAILY POWER CONSUMPTION — WATT–HOURS					
Dry 1	1673	1727	2023	1869	2599
Power Demand as against Cork Box = 100%		103.2%	120.9%	111.7%	155.3%
Wet 1	1835	2764	2589	2397	3891
5	1900	3784	3641	2943	4169
10	2078	4272	4499	3763	4540
15	2140	4433	4771	3970	4609
18	2300	4891	5410	4575	5121
Power Demand as against Cork Box = 100%		212.7%	235.2%	198.9%	222.7%
WATER ABSORBED — POUNDS					
Wet 5	26.8	131.0	122.8	110.5	159.6
10	41.6	169.8	198.8	177.8	212.4
15	50.6	190.3	228.5	209.3	227.1
18	54.9	203.5	266.0	236.3	267.6

In this table will be found not the whole story as to what happens to low-temperature insulation under service conditions, because, as indicated in the heading, these five boxes were without any surface protection on the hot side. But in this table there is an indication of the performance which is to be expected of cork insulation as against the four non-cork materials tested when they are "on their own" as regards moisture penetration. The non-cork boxes took up from almost four to well over five times as much water as the cork box and at the end of the test period the best of the non-cork boxes was consuming twice as much electric power as the cork box.

All of the non-cork materials tested were fibrous in structure and in such a comparative showing as appears in the above table is to be found the reason why cork—a cellular material—is the world's standard form of low-temperature insulating material.

The complete reports on the Association's testing described above have been published as *Low Temperature Insulation— Physical Properties Test Data* and *Low Temperature Insulation— Simulated Usage Test Data* (edited by the author of this volume).

APPENDIX C

CORK IN TIME OF WAR

To most people cork is probably a typical peace-time commodity. On the contrary, its importance in time of war for uses ranging from simple gaskets to ammunition plugs is so great that cork is now one of fifteen products classified by the Army and Navy Munitions Board as "critical materials." [1] Modern warfare is so completely mechanized that no nation can permit itself to be without or even to "run short" of those materials necessary for the construction of the machines and equipment with which modern civilized nations seek to destroy or dominate other civilized nations. Cork is such a material and, as we have seen, the United States must import its entire requirements. Hence it is classified as a critical material defined by the Munitions Board as follows:

Critical materials are those essential to national defense, the procurement problems of which in war would be less difficult than those of strategic materials either because they have a lesser degree of essentiality or are obtainable in more adequate quantities from domestic sources; and for which some degree of conservation and distribution control will be necessary.[2]

In explanation of the inclusion of cork in its list of critical materials, the Board says:

Owing to its many industrial and commercial uses a shortage of cork in a major emergency would entail serious difficulties. Even though substitutes are available and practical in a number of cases there are others whereby substitution might temporarily disrupt mass production practices or there may be a shortage of a particular substitution such as rubber, itself a strategic material. Conservation, substitution and at least some degree of control of cork stocks would be necessary in an emergency were we denied imports.

[1] As of early 1941, there are fourteen "strategic materials" (antimony, chromium, coconut shell char, manganese, manila fiber, mercury, mica, nickel, quartz crystal, quinine, rubber, silk, tin and tungsten) and fifteen "critical materials" (aluminum, asbestos, cork, graphite, hides, iodine, kapok, opium, optical glass, phenol, platinum, tanning materials, toluol, vanadium and wool).
[2] Cf. a pamphlet entitled *The Strategic and Critical Materials* published by the Army and Navy Munitions Board, Washington, D. C., 1940.

The actual administration of the problems and details connected with the strategic and critical materials is now being cleared through the Office of Production Management. So far as cork is concerned the OPM deals with the industry largely through the industry Association and to date has been primarily interested in:

1. Cork production and available supplies.
2. Available shipping facilities.
3. Inventories in the United States.
4. Monthly usage of cork.
5. The cork "outlook."

The last is, of course, the real problem—a problem at once of many answers, and a problem with only a Time answer. As of early 1941, the many answers are:

1. The 1940-1941 cork strip is only between one-half and two-thirds the average of recent years.

2. Little or none of the production of certain areas, notably those in North Africa, will be available without a change in the war controls now in force, and the industry needs this African cork to avoid a shortage.

3. As an offset to the decrease in production and available supplies, the demands of the warring nations will be less, leaving a larger "share" of the supply available to the United States.

4. Imports of raw cork since the War broke out (September 1939-December 1940) have continued in very satisfactory volume (see p. 22) but are beginning to reflect the reduced strip and the increasing difficulty of getting adequate shipping.

5. The relation between imports and usage throughout 1940 resulted in an increase of approximately 15% in the raw cork inventories within the United States on December 31, 1940, as compared with December 31, 1939, but reduced imports and increased usage during the first quarter of 1941 are cutting heavily into inventories.

6. Because the industry itself can finance the purchase and storage of all available cork and had a better inventory condition at the end of 1940 than at the end of 1939, the purchase of a stock pile (a Government-owned reserve supply) does not at present appear necessary, but, without African cork, some plan of conservation of stocks now seems unavoidable.

As of now (early 1941) these are the many answers to the problem of the cork outlook. They have been set down here for the immediate information of those interested and also as a matter of record. Years hence some casual reader, some student or some historian not yet born may read these many answers and will know how well or how badly we who are now struggling with the problem of cork forecast the answer which Time will have given.

APPENDIX D

ADDENDUM TO CHAPTER I

Another chapter in the history of the California cork trees referred to in the quotation from Dun's *International Review* on p. 1 was written during the summer of 1940.[1] The largest and most important of the California stands of cork trees are located at Chico in Butte County and in Napa County, but there are scattered trees throughout the surrounding areas. For a number of years prior to 1940, these trees had been under the close observation of Professor Woodbridge Metcalf, Extension Forester of the University of California,[2] and early in 1940, it

The cork stand at Chico, Butte County, California.

[1] The California stripping and planting project described in this section was sponsored by Mr. C. E. McManus, Sr., of Baltimore, Md., and was carried out by Prof. Woodbridge Metcalf and Mr. G. D. Greenan of San Francisco, who furnished the author with the material for this write-up. The library of the School of Forestry of Oregon State College at Corvallis, Ore., has on file a manuscript, *The Cork Oak: Past, Present and Future on the Pacific Coast*, submitted as a graduation thesis in June 1940 by Stuart W. Heintzelman, and mentioned here as another evidence of interest in the cork oak in our western States.

[2] Cf. Prof. Metcalf's monograph, *Cork Oak—A Forest Tree with Possibilities for California* written in 1929. (Out of print but can be read in the Monthly Bulletin of the California Department of Agriculture for October 1929.)

was decided that many of them were ready for stripping. The project was begun in July of that year and continued into October. Altogether 248 trees in Butte, Napa and Yolo Counties were stripped. The following summary reports the principal details of the stripping of the three different groups of trees:

	Chico Station	McGill Ranch	Others	All Trees
Number of trees	166	60	22	248
Av. diam. outside bark, in.	11.0	15.6	19.4	12.7
Av. diam. after stripping, in.	8.9	12.2	16.3	10.2
Av. thickness of cork, in.	1.05	1.7	1.5	1.25
Av. length of bole stripped, ft.	5.5	6.6	7.85	5.1
Total cork stripped, lbs.	3,783	4,999	1,778	10,560
Av. cork stripped per tree, lbs.	22.8	84.7	80.6	43.8
Age of trees, years	36	62	....	....

The trees at Chico are in a stand of about 400 planted in 1904. Those on the McGill Ranch near Oakville in Napa County are in a grove of 70 trees planted in 1878 by John Benson from acorns imported from Spain.[1] The McGill Ranch trees are therefore 70-odd years old; their average yield of about 85 pounds of cork is very low for trees of that age and is due largely to their never having been stripped or pruned.

[144]

Some of the trees stripped more easily than others.

The five tons of cork stripped were shipped to the laboratories of two large American cork companies for study and experimentation. The preliminary testing completed to date indicates the California product to be of excellent quality virgin cork, but it will take at least another generation before the quality and commercial usefulness of California cork can be definitely established.

[1] Scattered cork oaks are standing in California (and elsewhere in southern States) from plantings made between 1850 and 1860 of Spanish acorns distributed by the United States Patent Department. See Reports of the United States Commissioner of Patents for 1854 (pp. xxxiii-xxxiv), 1858 (pp. vi and 334-337) and 1859 (p. 14).

Present available quantities are of course completely inadequate to have any influence on the world supply or to make any impression on American requirements for cork. But a start has been made on a long-time program to change this. Supplementing the stripping operations described above a planting project has been started. About 300 available seedlings have already been planted or will be planted this spring. A large volume of acorns for propagation was gathered during the fall of 1940 and present plans anticipate that about 30,000 trees will soon be available for shipment to co-operating land owners. In time, the Mediterranean basin may not be the world's only source of cork, but it will take at least 30 years to tell how serious this California threat really is.

Except for a Brazilian source of cork substitute (mentioned below), this California project is at present the only known development which can be called a threat to the Mediterranean monopoly. During 1938 and 1939 the United States Department of Commerce conducted a world-wide survey to determine again whether or not there is a source either of natural cork or of cork substitutes outside the Mediterranean area. The results of the Department's survey made up from reports from its representatives throughout the world can be briefly summarized as follows:

1. No source of natural cork in commercial quantities exists outside the Mediterranean area. (It is known that in 1928 a quantity of French cork oak acorns was shipped to Russia for experimental planting in the Caucasus. The Department's report on this planting says: "It is understood that the experiments carried on in the Caucasus have been successful, but the embassy has been unable to obtain data relating to the plans, if any, which the Soviet authorities may have drawn up with regard to possible future cultivation on a commercial scale.")

Cork "log" stripped with only one vertical cut.

2. Here and there throughout the world there is a very limited local use of home-grown substitutes for cork. In Bolivia, for example, it is reported that the woods of three native trees are sometimes used as cork substitutes, and in Germany stoppers have been made of poplar and aspen. (The report refers to the use of Balsa wood [Ecuador, the principal producer] as a cork substitute for marine goods mentioned in Chapter VIII.)

3. Two cork substitutes with limited commercial development were found. In Brazil the bark of a native tree known as the Pao Santo was being manufactured into an insulating board resembling corkboard in weight and appearance. In Japan, the bark of a native tree known as the Abemaki is used as a cork substitute but, according to the report, "the bulk of the country's demand for cork materials is supplied from foreign sources." [1]

California and, perhaps, Russia are apparently therefore the only two potential sources of cork unless there are possibilities in the Pao Santo of Brazil. Several American manufacturers have experimented with this Brazilian tree bark, which at present offers small promise as a cork substitute because of the limited supply available and prohibitive transportation costs between Brazil and American ports.

[1] Publication of the Department's report is pending. It is expected to be available in the near future.

A weathered old cork oak at Norfolk, Va.
(Photograph taken in February 1941)

APPENDIX E

ADDENDUM TO CHAPTER III

THE uncertainty concerning the founding of the American cork industry has been greatly clarified since the first edition of this book was published. All attempts to clear up who started cork manufacturing in the United States and when led back, rather vaguely, to William King, known only to a few men now in the industry as scarcely more than the name of a man who had been in the cork business and who died "years ago some place in New Jersey." The paragraph in the first edition of this book on the founding of the American industry came to the attention of Miss Katharine L. McCormick, a local historian of Perth Amboy, N. J., who, from records and a King descendant (Mrs. Charles H. Aldrich of Elizabeth, N. J.), has established the fact that it was William King's father, Stephen, who founded the American cork industry in 1830 in New York City.[1]

NOS. 160-164 WATER STREET, NEW YORK CITY IN 1836
On this old New York City street at No. 192, Stephen King founded the first American cork factory in 1830.

[1] Mrs. Aldrich is a granddaughter of William King with whom she made her home, and from whom she frequently heard "chapters" of the King family history. In a letter to the author Miss McCormick writes: "She [Mrs. Aldrich] agrees that Stephen King . . . was really the founder [of the American cork industry] rather than her grandfather, William King."

[147]

Miss McCormick, who has a vivid childhood memory of William King as a local resident, writes as follows in the *Perth Amboy Evening News* for February 17, 1940:

> "With the idea of establishing a new industry in America there sailed from Rye, England, a little over a hundred years ago—in 1829 to be exact—a cork manufacturer named Stephen King. He settled with his wife and family in New York where he started the first cork factory in America. Longworth's New York Directory for the years 1831-1832 has his name listed thus: 'Stephen King & Co., Cork cutters, 192 Water street.'
>
> "After a year or two the words 'company' and 'cutters' disappear after the name and the listing is 'Stephen King, Corks.' In 1848 a new dealer in corks appears at the Water street address. It is William King. He is the son of Stephen. He is 30 years old now, for the family records show that the Kings left England in 1829 when the boy, William, was 11 years old. His home address is given for the next two years as 76 Madison street. Then in 1850 it changes to Perth Amboy."

Water Street is "downtown" in the oldest part of New York City. Now one block in from the East River, it runs north and south across such famous streets as Wall, Maiden Lane, John and Fulton. Its lower section was involved in New York's "Great Fire" of 1835 which completely destroyed all the buildings in an area covering seventeen blocks and ruined many of the insurance companies of the day.

According to Miss McCormick, William King continued in the cork business in Perth Amboy until 1909, except for a brief period in the eighteen-nineties. He died in 1915 at the age of 97. Stephen King died in 1842 in Halifax, Nova Scotia, shortly after arriving there apparently for the purpose of opening a cork factory.

INDEX

INDEX

Plumbing, uses of cork in, 129
Portugal: cork acreage and production, 12; stripping restrictions, 14; prices of cork from, 20
Prices: cork wood, 20; cork waste, 20; cork stoppers, 44
Printed linoleum, 103, 107

Quercus Suber, 1; *Q. Occidentalis*, 1 n.
Quintal, unit of cork weight, 18

Radiation, 132
Refrigerators, domestic, insulation in, 56 n.
Refugo, 15, 53
Regranulated cork, 61
Resilience: of cork, 6; of cork tile, 87
Resistance to moisture penetration: of cork, 6; of corkboard, 57; of cork marine products, 97
Romana, used for weighing, 17
Rome, ancient, use of cork in, 1, 2, 24, 95
Russia, as source of cork, 145

Sale of cork: on trees, 16; at auctions, 16-17; 1940 auction schedule, 17 n.
Scientific instruments and equipment, uses of cork in, 130
Scrims, linoleum manufacture, 104
Shoe products, 80, 131
Sirocco, 14, 24
Smith, John T., 25; discovers modern corkboard, 50
Sorting and grading: 17-18, 32; of cork stoppers, 39
Source of cork supply, 1, 11-13
Spain: cork acreage and production, 12; stopper industry begins in, 36
Spanish black, 115 n.
Specie corks, 40
Specific gravity of cork, 97
Sporting goods, cork, 48, 83, 130
Stability of cork, 9
Statistics: cork wood and cork waste imports, 22; American cork industry, 23, 27; cork stopper industry, 42; cork insulation industry, 66; cork composition industry, 84-85; cork tile industry, 91; cork marine goods industry, 99; linoleum and cork carpet industry, 112; cork and linoleum industries, 119; imports of cork products and linoleum, 120; exports of cork products and linoleum, 120
Stecher, Gilbert E., 3 n.
Stone, Junius H., 52
Stripping: first, 13; frequency of, 13;

restrictions, 14; period of, 15; how done, 15
Suberac, 71
Suberit, 71

Tariff Act of 1930, cork paragraph, 120
Testing: corkboard, physical properties, 134-136; on corkboard simulated usage conditions, 136-140
Tetrakaidecahedron, 4
Textile machinery and equipment, uses of cork in, 128
Thermal conductivity: of cork, 7; testing to determine, 134-135
Thomas, Pearl Edwin, 1 n., 50 n., 52 n.
Thomson, Sir William (Lord Kelvin), 4 n.
Tunisia, cork acreage and production, 12

United States: attempts to grow cork in, 1, 144 n.; share of world cork production, 18; ports of entry, 19; imports of wood and waste, 22; cork industry established in, 23; linoleum industry established in, 102; contributions to development of cork industry, 121
Ure, Andrew, 2 n.
Uses of cork: automotive and transportation, 125-126; in electrical equipment, 126; food machinery and equipment, 127; glass machinery and equipment, 127; household equipment, 127; lubricating equipment and bearings, 128; measuring, handling and dispensing of gases and liquids, 128; musical instruments, 126; office and store equipment, 129; packaging equipment and materials, 129; plumbing, heating, cooling and ventilating, 129; scientific instruments and equipment, 130; sporting goods and toys, 130; textile machinery and equipment, 128; miscellaneous, 130-131

Vapor pressure differential, 138
Ventilating, uses of cork in, 129
Vibration absorbing property of cork, 8, 61-62
Virgin cork, 15, 53

Walton, Frederick, 101
Waste: explained, 21; imports of, 22; blocker and shavings, 46; valuable by-product, 48
Weights used in cork trade, 18
Wolfe, John K., 10 n.
World production of cork, 11-13

Zeeuw, Carl Henri de, 4 n.

[151]